Algebra Connections
Preliminary Edition, Version 2.0

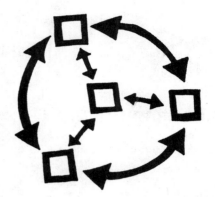

Managing Editor

Evra Baldinger
Phillip and Sala Burton Academic High School
San Francisco, CA

Contributing Editors

Joanne da Luz
The Life Learning Academy
San Francisco, CA

Patricia King
Holmes Junior High School
Davis, CA

Lara Lomac
Phillip and Sala Burton Academic High School
San Francisco, CA

Bob Petersen
Sacramento High School
Sacramento, CA

Ward Quincey
Gideon Hausner Jewish Day School
Palo Alto, CA

Michael Titelbaum
University of California
Berkeley, CA

Illustrator

Kevin Coffey
San Francisco, CA

Technical Assistants

Erica Andrews
Bethany Armstrong
Elizabeth Burke
Carrie Cai

Elizabeth Fong
Rebecca Harlow
Michael Leong

Program Directors

Leslie Dietiker
Phillip and Sala Burton Academic High School
San Francisco, CA

Brian Hoey
Christian Brothers High School
Sacramento, CA

Judy Kysh, Ph.D.
Departments of Mathematics and Education
San Francisco State University

Tom Sallee, Ph.D.
Department of Mathematics
University of California, Davis

Credits for Pilot Edition

Managing Editor
Leslie Dietiker
Phillip and Sala Burton Academic High School
San Francisco, CA

Contributing Editors
Evra Baldinger
Phillip and Sala Burton Academic High School
San Francisco, CA

Carlos Cabana
San Lorenzo High School
San Lorenzo, CA

John Cooper
Del Oro High School
Sacramento, CA

David Gulick
Phillips Exeter Academy
Exeter, NH

Bob Petersen
Sacramento High School
Sacramento, CA

Barbara Shreve
San Lorenzo High School
San Lorenzo, CA

Michael Titelbaum
The College Preparatory School
Oakland, CA

Technical Assistants
Eric Baxter
Keith Lee

1 2 3 4 5 6 7 8 9   08 07 06 05 04   Version 2.0

Printed in the United States of America   ISBN 1-931287-39-2

A Note to Students:

Welcome to a new year of math! In this course, you will be exposed to a powerful set of mathematical tools called algebra. As a set of tools, algebra is the foundation of higher mathematics—future courses will build from what you learn here. Algebra is also a way of thinking: a way of investigating new situations, discovering relationships, and figuring out what strategies can be used to solve problems. Learning to think this way is useful both in mathematical contexts and in situations outside the classroom.

In meeting the challenges of algebra, you will not be working alone. During this course you will collaborate with other students as a member of a study team. Working in a team means speaking up and interacting with others. You will explain your ideas, listen to what others have to say, and ask questions if there is something you do not understand. In algebra, a single problem can often be solved many ways. You will see problems in different ways than your teammates do. Each of you has something to contribute while you work on the lessons in this course.

Together, your team will complete problems and activities that will help you discover new mathematical ideas and methods. Your teacher will support you as you work, but will not take away your opportunity to think and investigate for yourself. Each topic will be revisited many times and connected to other topics. If something is not clear to you the first time you work with it, you will have more chances to build your understanding as the course continues.

Learning math this way has a significant advantage: as long as you actively participate, make sure everyone in your study team is involved, and ask good questions, you will find yourself understanding mathematics at a deeper level than ever before. By the end of this course, you will have a powerful set of mathematical tools at your disposal. You will see how these tools connect with each other so that you can use them together to solve new problems. With your teammates you will meet mathematical challenges you would not have known how to approach before.

We wish you well and are confident that you will enjoy learning algebra!

Sincerely,

The CPM Team

Algebra
Connections
Table of Contents

Student Edition

CHAPTER 7   Linear Relationships

Chapter 7 will complete the focus on linear equations that started in Chapter 1 and continued through Chapters 3, 4, and 6. In this chapter, you will analyze the geometric meaning of slope and explore the idea of slope as a rate of change. You will also use trend lines to make predictions from existing data about future events.

In this chapter, you will learn:

➢ How to find the slope (steepness) of a line given its equation, its graph, or any two points on the line.

➢ How the slopes of parallel and perpendicular lines are related.

➢ How slopes can represent rates of change in real-life applications.

➢ How to find the equation of a trend line to fit linear data.

➢ How to find the slope of a line without graphing.

Guiding Questions

Think about these questions throughout this chapter:

What is slope?

What is a rate?

How can we find the equation of a line?

How are the slopes of two lines related?

Chapter Outline

Section 7.1   In this section, you will find equations of lines that fit data. You will learn how to measure the steepness of a line on a graph. You will also study the difference between lines that point upward, lines that point downward, and lines that are horizontal.

Section 7.2   This section investigates situations where slope represents a rate in a real-life context, culminating in an activity called The Big Race. In this section you will also discover a method for finding the equation of a line when given only two points on the line.

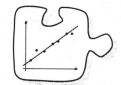

Section 7.3   The chapter ends with an activity in which you will use your understanding of slope and $y = mx + b$ to solve problems.

7.1.1 How do we see lines?

$y = mx + b$ and Growth

In this chapter, you will learn to find the equation of a line using different pieces of information. Today's lesson will review connections you made in previous chapters by challenging you to find equations for lines from graphs, tables, and patterns. As you work on today's problems, keep these questions in mind:

What do you know about the line?

How can you see the growth?

How can you verify that your answer is correct?

7*1.   **Your Task:** With your team, find the equation (and the correct window) that you can enter into your grapher to create the graph at right:

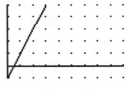

Does everyone in your team have a graph that looks the same? Did everyone use the same equation? Did everyone use the same "window" settings? Record the equation and the window settings that you used.

7*2.   THE LINE FACTORY–Part One

The Line Factory is having a serious problem: too many customers have placed orders, and then received a line different from the one they wanted! The factory has hired your team to eliminate this problem. Today, working in pairs, you will test each other's ability to place and confirm an order for the lines your customers want.

Step One: Customers Create an Order
First, you and your partner will create an order for a line. At this company, orders come in a variety of forms. To test your ability to handle different types of orders, one pair in your team will submit its order as an $x \rightarrow y$ table, and the other pair will submit its order in the form of a tile pattern.

Continued on next page→

7*2.   *Continued from previous page*

> **Table creators:** Be sure the points in your $x \to y$ table make a **linear** pattern! The x-values in your table must increase by 1 each time, but the y-values should grow by some number other than 1.
>
> **Pattern creators:** Draw three figures in your pattern, labeled with their figure numbers. Be sure that you create a **linear** pattern!

Step Two: Salespeople Receive and Analyze the Order
Switch orders with the other pair in your team. Your job is to check the order you have been given for accuracy. Find an equation for the order and graph that equation on your grapher. Adjust the window so you can be sure your line fits all of the information you were given.

Step Three: Salespeople Confirm the Order with the Customers
To make sure your customers (the other pair in your team) get the line they want, show them the graph on your grapher. **Justify** to them that this line fits the information they gave you. As part of your justification, show how the growth on your graph is the same as the growth in their order. (You will need to do this twice in your team, once with your pair as salespeople and once with your pair as customers.)

7*3.   THE LINE FACTORY–Part Two: CALCULATOR DESIGN CHALLENGE

Congratulations! You have passed the Line Factory training program and have received your first order from a real customer. Straightedge Pictures needs several lines for their new animated movie. They have sent these pictures of the lines they need for three different scenes:

Scene 1   Scene 2   Scene 3

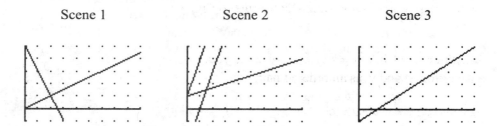

Your Task: Work with your team to find the equations that create the lines needed for each scene. (You should use the same window settings that you found in problem 7*1.)

Algebra Connections: Chapter 7

In Chapter 6, you learned to solve a system of equations using the substitution method. This method is reviewed below.

METHODS AND MEANINGS

The Substitution Method

Previously, we used substitution as an algebraic way to find the point of intersection for two linear equations. In those problems, the two equations were always in y-form. However, substitution can be used even if the equations are not in y-form.

Given:
$$x = -3y + 1$$
$$4x - 3y = -11$$

Use substitution to rewrite the two equations as one.

We can then write $4(-3y + 1) - 3y = -11$ by replacing x with $(-3y + 1)$.

$$x = \boxed{-3y + 1}$$

$$4(\;) - 3y = -11$$

$$4(-3y + 1) - 3y = -11$$

Simplify.

$$-12y + 4 - 3y = -11$$

Next, solve the equation for y.

$$-15y + 4 = -11$$

To find the point of intersection, substitute to find the other value.

$$-15y = -15$$

Substitute $y = 1$ into $x = -3y + 1$ and write your answer for x and y as an ordered pair.

$$y = 1$$

You should also substitute $y = 1$ into $4x - 3y = -11$ to verify that either original equation may be used to find the second coordinate.

$$x = -3(1) + 1 = -2$$

$$(-2, 1)$$

7*4.   A tile pattern grows so that each new figure has 7 tiles more than the figure before. If Figure 2 has 33 tiles, write a rule that represents the number of tiles in each figure. Then use your rule to find out how many tiles Figure 25 has.

7*5.   Match the system of equations in the left column with its solution in the right column.

a. $6x - y = 4$
       $3x + y = 5$ 1.   (0, -4)

b. $x = y + 4$
       $2x + 3y = -12$ 2.   (3, 7)

c. $5x - 2y = 1$
       $y = 2x + 1$ 3.   (1, 2)

7*6.   Graph $y = -\frac{1}{2}x + 6$. Find its x- and y-intercepts.

7*7.   Use proportions to solve each of the problems below.

a.   At the zoo, three adult lions eat 250 pounds of food a day. If two more adult lions joined the group, how much food would the zoo need to provide each day?

b.   Byron can read 45 pages in an hour. How long will it take for him to read the new 700-page Terry Cotter book?

7*8.   Solve each equation below for the indicated variable.

a. $4x - 2 + y = 6 - 2x$ for y.

b. $4x - 2 + y = 6 - 2x$ for x.

c. $3(6 - x) + 2x = 15$ for x.

7*9.   Little Evan has 356 stuffed animals, all of which are either teddy bears or dogs. He has 17 more than twice as many dogs as teddy bears. How many teddy bears does he own? Write and solve an equation (or a system of equations) to solve this problem. Be sure to define your variable(s).

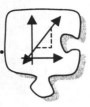

7.1.2 How can I use graphs and equations?

Using Graphs and Equations to Make Predictions

You have learned to find and **extend** patterns in data and make predictions using rules, equations, and graphs. Today you will **apply** these math tools to a real situation in which your data does not make a perfect pattern.

7*10.   Review problem 1*15, stated below.

Have you heard about Euclid's Revenge, the new roller coaster? It's so big, fast, and scary that people are already starting to talk. Some people are worried about the tunnel that thrills riders with its very low ceiling.

The closest the ceiling of the tunnel ever comes to the seat of the roller coaster car is 200 cm. Although no accidents have been reported yet, rumors have started that very tall riders have been seriously injured as they went through the tunnel with their arms raised over their heads. Unfortunately, the rumors are spreading and tall people have stopped riding the coaster. Determine if the roller coaster is safe for all riders.

a.   Explain in your own words what this problem was about.

b.   Review the prediction you made for this problem and explain why your prediction makes sense.

7*11.   Today you will use your new knowledge about graphs and equations to solve the problem of Euclid's Revenge. Your teacher will distribute graphing calculators or instruct you to use a computer. Enter your data comparing students' height to their reach (both in centimeters) into your grapher.

      a.   What window should you use to be able to see all of your data in a scatter plot? Set up the appropriate window and make a scatter plot with your grapher.

      b.   Is this plot useful for making predictions? Why or why not? If not, how could you change the plot to make it more useful?

7*12.   You now have experience with finding equations from tables and graphing equations. You will find the equation that you think works best for your data. Once you have the equation, you will be able to verify or change your prediction.

Set the window on your grapher to show the x-axis from 0 to your highest x-value and the y-axis from 0 to your highest y-value.

      a.   Guess an equation that you think might come close to your data. Enter the equation into your grapher and graph it in the same window as your data. Did you come close?

      b.   Change the numbers in your equation to numbers you think might better fit the data. Graph the equation again and see what happens. Keep trying new numbers until you find an equation that you think comes close to fitting the data. What is your equation?

      c.   Now reset the window to zoom in on your data. Does your equation still seem to fit the data well? If not, adjust your equation until you are satisfied with how it fits the data.

      d.   Zoom back out and find the y-intercept. What does this point represent? Does this make sense? Change your equation if necessary so that your equation makes sense at $x = 0$.

7*13.   Now that you have an equation for your data and its graph, revisit your prediction about Yao Ming's safety on the roller coaster in problem 1*15.

      a.   Use your equation to decide whether Yao Ming will be safe. Show all of your work.

      b.   Does your result agree with your earlier prediction? If not, what changed?

      c.   Use your grapher to confirm your decision.

In Chapter 6, you learned how to solve a system of equations using the elimination method. This method is reviewed below.

METHODS AND MEANINGS

The Elimination Method for Solving Systems of Equations

One method of solving systems of equations is the **Elimination Method**. This method involves adding or subtracting both sides of two equations to eliminate a variable. We can combine equations this way because balance is maintained when equal amounts are added to both sides of an equation. For example, if $a = b$ and $c = d$, then if we add a and c we will get the same result as adding b and d. Thus, $a + c = b + d$.

Consider the system of linear equations shown at right. Notice that when both sides of the equations are added together, the sum of the x-terms is zero and so the x-terms are eliminated. (Be sure to write both equations so that x is above x, y is above y, and the constants are similarly matched.)

$$3x + 2y = 14$$
$$\underline{-3x + 5y = 14}$$
$$\frac{7y}{7} = \frac{28}{7}$$
$$y = 4$$

Now that we have one equation with one variable ($7y = 28$), we can solve for y by dividing both sides by 7. To find x, we can substitute our answer for y into one of the original equations, as shown at right. We can then test our solution for x and y by substituting both values into the other equation to verify that $-3x + 5y = 14$.

$$3x + 2(4) = 14$$
$$3x + 8 = 14$$
$$3x = 6$$
$$x = 2$$

Since we found that $x = 2$ and $y = 4$ is a solution to both equations, we can state that the two lines cross at the point (2, 4).

$$-3(2) + 5(4) = 14 \checkmark$$

Review & Preview

7*14.   Evaluate each expression for a when $a = \frac{2}{3}$.

a. $24a$

b. $3a$

c. $\frac{a}{0}$

d. $\frac{0}{a}$

Linear Relationships

7*15.   Find the distance between the following pairs of points.

      a.   (3, 7) and (8, 7)   b.   (-13, 7) and (8, 7)

      c.   (x, 7) and (c, 7)   d.   (5, 2) and (5, 38)

      e.   (5, -4) and (5, 34)   f.   (5, y) and (5, f)

7*16.   Solve.

      a. $3x - 7(4 + 2x) = -x + 2$ b. $-5x + 2 - x + 1 = 0$

7*17.   The figures below are **similar** (meaning they have the same shape). Use the information given about the lengths of the sides to solve for x and y.

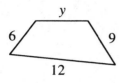 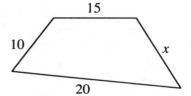

7*18.   Find the solution for each system of equations below, if a solution exists. If there is not a single solution, explain why not. Be sure to check your solution, if possible.

      a. $\begin{aligned} x + 4y &= 2 \\ 3x - 4y &= 10 \end{aligned}$ b. $\begin{aligned} 2x + 4y &= -10 \\ x &= -2y - 5 \end{aligned}$

7*19.   The growth of a baby's length can be determined by the equation $l = 23 + 1.5t$, where l represents the length of the baby in inches and t represents the age of the baby in months.

      a.   How fast is the baby growing each month? How can you tell?

      b.   How long was the baby when it was born? How can you tell?

      c.   How long will the baby be when it is 3 months old?

      d.   If the baby was born in January, during what month will it be 39.5 inches long?

7.1.3 How can we measure steepness?

Measuring Steepness: An Introduction to Slope

You have been investigating what factors determine the steepness and position of a line and have seen that m in a $y = mx + b$ equation determines the direction of a line on a graph. In this lesson you will use all of your knowledge about m to determine the accurate value of m in an equation when you see the graph of a line.

During this lesson, ask your teammates the following focus questions:

What does m tell you about a line?

What makes lines steeper? What makes lines less steep?

How is growth related to steepness?

7*20. In Chapter 4 you worked with tile patterns and **made connections** between tile patterns and graphs. Think back on your work from that chapter to answer these questions about the tile patterns A and B represented in the graph at right.

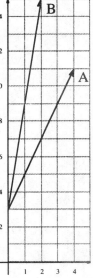

a. By looking at the graph, what statements can you make about the two tile patterns? What do the patterns have in common? What is different? Be specific.

b. On the Resource Page you receive from your teacher, draw growth triangles for each line. If available, use different colors for the triangles on each line. Label each triangle with its dimensions.

c. What does the steepness of a line tell you about the growth of the tile pattern?

d. Write an equation (rule) for each tile pattern.

7*21.   The graph below shows a line for a tile pattern you may recognize from Chapter 4. What is the growth factor for this line? That is, how many tiles are added each time the figure number is increased by 1? Explain how you determined the growth factor.

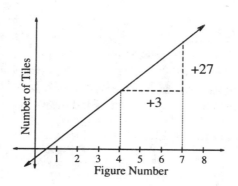

7*22.   The growth triangles in problem 7*21 are also called **slope triangles**. **Slope** is a measure of the steepness of a line. It is the ratio of the vertical distance to the horizontal distance of a slope triangle. The vertical part of the triangle is called Δy (read "change in y"), while the horizontal part of the triangle is called Δx (read "change in x"). Note that "Δ" is the Greek "delta" that is often used to represent a difference or change.

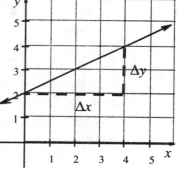

a.   What is the vertical distance (Δy) for this slope triangle?

b.   What is the horizontal distance (Δx) for this slope triangle?

c.   Find this graph on the Resource Page. Draw miniature slope triangles for this line that have a horizontal distance $\Delta x = 1$. Use one of these mini-triangles to find the slope (growth factor) for this line. What did you do with Δy and Δx to find the slope?

d.   What is the equation of this line?

7*23.   Find the line graphed at right with slope triangles
         A, B, and C on the Resource Page.

         a.   Find the slope using slope triangles A and B.
               What do you notice?

         b.   What is the vertical distance (Δy) of slope
               triangle C? Explain your reasoning.

         c.   Draw a slope triangle on the line with a
               horizontal distance (Δx) of 1 unit. Find the
               vertical distance (Δy) of this new triangle.
               What do you notice?

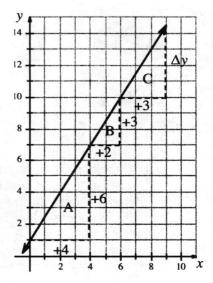

7*24.   What is special about the line that has $\Delta y = 0$? How can you describe a line for which
         $\Delta x = 0$? Draw a diagram for each case to demonstrate your answer.

7*25.   Michaela is trying to find the slope of the line shown
         at right. Her teammate, Cynthia, believes that $\Delta y = 3$
         because the triangle is three units tall, while her other
         teammate, Essie, thinks that $\Delta y = -3$ because the
         triangle is three units tall and the line is pointing
         downward.

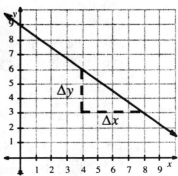

         a.   With whom do you agree and why?

         b.   When writing the slope of the line, Michaela
               noticed that Cynthia wrote $\frac{-3}{4}$ on her paper
               while Essie wrote $-\frac{3}{4}$. She asked, "Are these ratios equal?" Discuss this with
               your team and answer her question.

         c.   Find the equation of Michaela's line.

 METHODS AND MEANINGS

Introduction to Slope

Slope is a measure of the steepness of a line. It is the ratio of the vertical distance to the horizontal distance of a slope triangle. The vertical part of the triangle is called Δy (read "change in y"), while the horizontal part of the triangle is called Δx (read "change in x").

Note that "Δ" is the Greek letter "delta" that is often used to represent a difference or change.

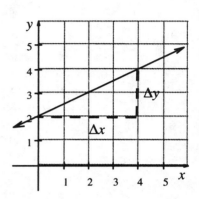

7*26.   What shape will the graph of $y = x^2 + 2$ be? How can you tell? **Justify** your prediction by making a table and graphing $y = x^2 + 2$ on graph paper.

7*27.   Carol has two rose bushes: one with red flowers and another with yellow. Her red rose bush has three times as many flowers as her yellow rose bush. Combined, they have 124 flowers. How many of each color flower does she have? Write an equation (or a system of equations) and solve.

7*28.   Do all lines eventually cross the x-axis? If not, provide a rule and a graph of a line that does not have an x-intercept.

7*29.   For each equation below, solve for x and check your answer.

   a. $10(2x - 1) = 100$

   b. $\frac{1}{3}x - 6 = 8$

   c. $(x - 2)(x + 1) = x^2 + 4x$

   d. $9x - 21 + 9 = 2(5 - x)$

7*30.   Write and solve an equation (or a system of equations) for the situation below. Define your variables and write your solution as a sentence.

Jennifer has a total of four and a half hours to spend on the beach swimming and playing volleyball. The time she spends playing volleyball will be twice the amount of time she spends swimming. How long will she do each activity?

7*31.   Use a generic rectangle to multiply the expressions below. Write your answer as a product and as a sum.

a. $(5x + 3)(x - 7)$

b. $-6x(4x - 3)$

7.1.4 How steep is it?

Comparing Δy and Δx

In Lesson 7.1.3, you discovered how to use the dimensions of a slope triangle to measure the steepness of a line. In this lesson, you will use the idea of stairs to understand slope even better. You will examine the difference between positive and negative slopes and will learn how to draw a line when given information about Δx and Δy.

During the lesson, ask your teammates the following focus questions:

How can you tell if m is positive or negative?

What makes lines steeper? What makes lines less steep?

How is steepness on a graph related to growth?

7*32.   One way to think about slope or growth triangles is as stair steps on a line.

a.   Picture yourself climbing (or descending) the stairs from left to right on each of the lines on the graph below right. Of lines A, B, and C, which is the steepest? Which is the least steep?

b.   Examine line D. What direction is it traveling from left to right? What should we use for Δy to represent this direction?

Continued on next page→

7*32. *Continued from previous page*

    c.   On the Resource Page, find the graph for problem 7*32 and label the legs of one of the slope triangles on each line. Write a sentence summarizing how to use these two dimensions to calculate the slope. Then, find the slope of each line.

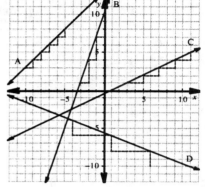

    d.   How does the slope relate to the steepness of the graph?

    e.   Cora answered part (d) above with "The steeper the line, the greater the slope number." Is she correct? If so, use lines A through D to support her statement. If not, change her statement to make it correct.

7*33. Find the graph for problem 7*33 on the Resource Page provided by your teacher.

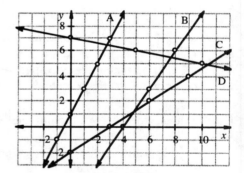

    a.   Which is the steepest line? Which is steeper, line B or C?

    b.   Draw slope triangles for lines A, B, C, and D using the highlighted points on each line. Label Δx and Δy for each.

    c.   Match each line with its slope using the list below. Note: You will have slopes left over.

$$m = 6 \qquad m = 2 \qquad m = -\tfrac{1}{5} \qquad m = \tfrac{3}{2}$$

$$m = 5 \qquad m = -\tfrac{2}{3} \qquad m = -5 \qquad m = \tfrac{2}{3}$$

    d.   In what direction would a line with slope $\tfrac{-3}{5}$ point? How do you know?

    e.   In what direction would a line with slope $\tfrac{-5}{3}$ point? How do you know? How would it be different from the line in part (d)?

7*34.   Examine lines A, B, and C on the graph at right.
         For each line, decide if the slope is positive or
         negative. Then, draw and label slope triangles on
         your Resource Page and calculate the slope.

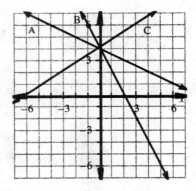

7*35.   On graph paper, graph a line to match each description below. Label each line with its
         slope.

         a.   A line that has $\Delta y = 6$ and $\Delta x = 1$.

         b.   A line that goes up 3 each time it goes over 5.

         c.   A line that has $\Delta x = 4$ and $\Delta y = -6$.

         d.   A line that has $\Delta y = 0$ and $\Delta x = 3$.

7*36.   What happens to the slope when the slope triangles
         are different sizes? For example, the line at right has
         three different slope triangles drawn as shown.

         a.   Find the slope using each of the slope triangles.
               What do you notice?

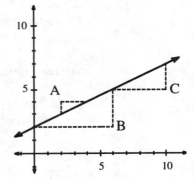

         b.   The triangle labeled A is drawn above the line.
               Does the fact that it is above the line instead of
               below it affect the slope of the line?

         c.   On the Resource Page provided by your teacher, draw another slope triangle for
               this line so that $\Delta x = 1$. What is the height (Δy) of this new slope triangle?

7*37.   Think back over the work you have done for the last two lessons. Use the ideas you have developed in class to answer the following questions as a Learning Reflection. Label this entry "Positive, Negative, and Zero Slope" and label it with today's date.

- *When is the slope of a line positive?*

- *When is the slope of a line negative?*

- *When is the slope of a line zero?*

- *What do you know about Δy and Δx for each kind of slope (positive, negative and zero)?*

Methods and Meanings

Solving Systems by Elimination
Part Two

Math Notes

Suppose we want to solve this system of equations:

Again, our task is to <u>eliminate</u> either x or y when we add the equations together. In this case we need to do something to BOTH equations before we add them. To eliminate y we can multiply the first equation by 3 and multiply the second equation by -2 to get:

$3x + 2y = 11$
$4x + 3y = 14$

$9x + 6y = 33$
$-8x - 6y = -8$

We chose 3 and –2 so that now we can eliminate the y terms by adding the two new equations:

$9x + 6y = 33$
$-8x - 6y = -28$
—————————
$x = 5$

Now we know $x = 5$ and can substitute to find that $y = -2$. Therefore, the solution to the system of equations is (5, -2).

You could also solve the system by multiplying the first equation by 4 and the second equation by -3. In this case you would have first eliminated x.

7*38. When Yoshi graphed the lines $y = 2x + 3$ and $y = 2x - 2$, she got the graph shown at right.

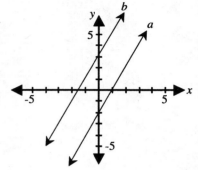

    a. Which line at right matches which equation above?

    b. Yoshi wants to add the line $y = 2x + 1$ to her graph. Predict where it would lie and sketch a graph to show its position. **Justify** your prediction.

    c. Where would the line $y = -2x + 1$ lie? Again, **justify** your prediction and add the graph of this line to your graph from part (b).

7*39. Find the point of intersection for each system of linear equations below. Be sure to check your solutions. Which method did you use for each system and why?

    a.
$$5x - y = 2$$
$$3x + y = -10$$

    b.
$$6x + 2y = 7$$
$$4x + y = 4$$

    c.
$$5x + 2y = 7$$
$$2y + 5x = 7$$

7*40. Solve each of the following equations.

    a. $2x + 8 = 3x - 4$

    b. $1.5(w + 2) = 3 + 2w$

    c. $8(x + 6) + 23 = 7$

    d. $3(2x - 7) = 5x + 17 + x$

7*41.   Copy and complete these generic rectangles on your paper. Then write the area of each as a **product** of the length and width and as a **sum** of the parts.

a.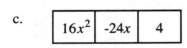

b.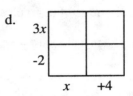

c.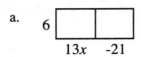

d.

7*42.   When Malcolm hops 15 times down the hallway, he travels 18 feet. How many times would he need to hop to travel to class (66 feet away)?

7*43.   On graph paper, graph a line with y-intercept $(0, -4)$ and x-intercept $(3, 0)$. Find the equation of the line.

7.1.5 How do Δy and Δx determine slope?

More on Slope

Today you will complete your focus on finding slope and using slope and the y-intercept to find the equation of a line. During this lesson, ask your teammates the following focus questions:

Is there enough information to graph the line?

How are parallel lines related?

How can I find the slope without graphing?

7*44.   **WHAT'S MY LINE?**

Below you will find information about several lines. If possible, graph each line and find its equation. If you do not have enough information to draw one line, draw at least three lines that fit the given criteria.

a.   Line A goes through (2, 5).

b.   Line B has a slope of -3 and goes through the origin (the point (0, 0)).

c.   Line C goes through points (2, 8) and (3, 10).

d.   Line D has a slope of 4.

e.   Line E goes through the point (8, -1) with a slope of $-\frac{3}{4}$.

f.   To graph a line and find its equation, what information do you need?

7*45.   **SLOPES OF PARALLEL LINES**

On graph paper, graph the line $y = \frac{1}{2}x - 3$.

a.   On the same set of axes, draw another line that is parallel to $y = \frac{1}{2}x - 3$. What is the slope of this line? Explain how you know.

b.   What do you notice about the slope of parallel lines?

c.   Use this idea to draw a line parallel to $y = -2x + 5$ through the point (0, -5).

d.   Now draw a line parallel to $y = \frac{1}{2}x - 3$ through the point (2, -5). Find its rule.

7*46.   **FINDING THE SLOPE OF A LINE WITHOUT GRAPHING**

While finding the slope of a line that goes through the points (6, 5) and (3, 7), Gloria figured that $\Delta y = -2$ and $\Delta x = 3$ without graphing.

a.   Explain how Gloria could find the horizontal and vertical distance of the slope triangle without graphing. Draw a sketch of the line and validate her method.

b.   What is the slope of the line?

Continued on next page →

7*46. *Continued from previous page*

c. Use Gloria's method (without graphing) to find the slope of the line that goes through the points (4, 15) and (2, 11).

d. Use Gloria's method to find the slope of the line that goes through the points (28, 86) and (34, 83).

e. Another student found the slope from part (d) to be 2. What error did that student make?

7*47. SLOPE CHALLENGE

What is the steepest line possible? What is its slope? Be ready to **justify** your statements.

METHODS AND MEANINGS

MATH NOTES

The Slope of a Line

The **slope** of a line is a measure of the rate at which the y-value changes in relation to the x-value. It indicates both how steep the line is and its direction.

$$\text{slope} = \frac{\text{vertical change}}{\text{horizontal change}} = \frac{\Delta y}{\Delta x}$$

Note that lines that point upward from left to right have positive slope, while lines that point downward from left to right have negative slope. A horizontal line has zero slope, while a vertical line has an undefined slope. The slope of a line is denoted by the letter m when using the $y = mx + b$ equation of a line.

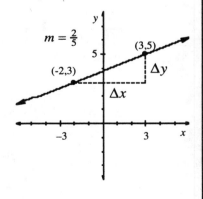

To calculate the slope of a line, pick two points on the line, draw the slope triangle (as shown in the example at right), determine Δx and Δy, and then write the slope ratio. You can verify that your slope correctly resulted in a negative or positive value based on its direction.

Algebra Connections: Chapter 7

7*48.   Sam and Jimmica have both taken a speed-reading class and have been assigned to read a 300-page novel. Jimmica started reading at noon and read 10 pages per minute. Sam was on page 62 at noon and read 8 pages per minute. Will Jimmica ever catch up to Sam? Explain how you found your answer.

7*49.   Consider this system of equations:

$$y = 2x - 8$$
$$y = -\tfrac{2}{3}x$$

   a.   Use your knowledge of $y = mx + b$ to graph the lines without tables.

   b.   Use the graph to find the point of intersection.

   c.   Confirm this point of intersection by solving the system algebraically.

7*50.   Find the slope of the lines described below without graphing.

   a.   A line through the points (4, 1) and (2, 5).

   b.   A line through the origin and the point (10, 5).

   c.   A vertical line (one that travels "up and down") through the point (6, -5).

   d.   A line through the points (1, 6) and (10, 6).

7*51.   Solve the equations below for x. Check each solution by substituting the answer back into the equation.

   a. $4(2 - x) + 3x = x$ b. $x^2 - 5x + 2 = (x - 3)(x - 2)$

   c. $\frac{3}{x} = 6$ d. $-(-2x + 3) = -(-5)$

7*52. Solve the equations below for the variable indicated.

a. $6x - 3y = 12$ for y

b. $y = -2x + 4$ for x

c. $4 - 2(3x + 2) = 4x - 10$ for x

d. $\frac{3-x}{4} = \frac{5}{2}$ for x

7*53. Graph the curve $y = 3x^2 - 6x - 24$ using x-values between -3 and 5 on graph paper. What are the x- and y-intercepts?

7.2.1 What is the equation of the line?

Equation of a Line in Context

Today you will start to look at slope as a measurement of rate. Today's activity ties together the equation of a line and motion. Look for ways to **connect** what you know about m and b as you have fun.

7*54. SLOPE WALK

Congratulations! The President of the Line Factory has approached your class with a special challenge: she now wants a way to find the equation of a line generated when a customer walks in front of a motion detector. That way, a customer can simply walk a line to order it from the factory.

Your Task: Once a motion detector has been set up with the correct software, have a volunteer walk **away** from the motion detector at a *constant* rate. In other words, he or she should walk the same speed the entire time. Then, once a graph is generated, find the equation of the line. Also find the equation of a line formed when a different volunteer walks **toward** the motion detector at a constant rate.

Discussion Points

What is this problem about?

What do you expect the first graph to look like? Why?

What will be different about the two graphs?

How does the volunteer's speed affect the graph?

7*55.   WALK THE WALK

To impress the President, you have decided to **reverse** the process: write instructions for a client on how to walk in front of the motion detector in order to create a graph for a given rule.

Each team in the class will be assigned one or two rules from the list below. Then, as a team, decide how to walk so that you will get the graph for your rule. After the entire team understands how to walk, one member will try to graph the line by walking in front of the motion detector. Pay close attention to detail! Your team only has two tries!

a. $y = 3x + 2$ b. $y = -x + 10$

c. $y = 6$ d. $y = 2x + 4$

e. $y = -2x + 13$ f. $y = x + 5$

g. $y = -0.5x + 15$ h. $y = 1.5x + 3$

7*56.   Write a memo to the President of the Line Factory explaining why you cannot use a motion detector to collect the data plotted below. The *x*-axis represents time, and the *y*-axis represents the distance from the motion detector in feet.

a.   b.

7*57.   The graph at right represents the number of tiles in a tile pattern.

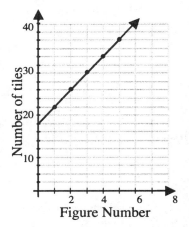

a.   Based on the information in the graph, how many tiles are being added each time (that is, what is the growth factor of the pattern)? Pay close attention to the scale of the axes.

b.   How many tiles are in Figure 0?

c.   How would the line change if the pattern grew by 12 tiles each time instead?

7*58.   On July 4th, Disneyland had 67,000 visitors and collected roughly $2,814,000. How much money should Disney expect to receive on New Year's Day, when park attendance reaches 71,000 people?

7*59.   Solve the system of equations at right.

$$y = \tfrac{2}{3}x - 4$$
$$2x - 3y = 10$$

a.   What does your solution tell you about the relationship between the lines?

b.   Solve the second equation for y.

c.   Does the slope of each line confirm your statement in part (a)? Explain how.

7*60.   Find the equation of each of the lines graphed at right. Then, confirm algebraically that (1, 1) is the point of intersection.

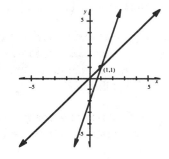

7*61.   Dominic simplified an expression using the Distributive Property and got this result: $15x^2 - 5x$. Can you find a possible expression that he started with?

7*62.   On graph paper, graph the line through the points (-6, 3) and (-3, -1).

a.   What is the slope of the line?

b.   What is the y-intercept?

c.   Find the equation of the line.

7.2.2 What does slope represent?

• •

Slope as a Measurement of Rate

Today you will focus on the meaning of slope in various contexts. What does a slope represent?
How can you use it?

7*63.   THE BIG RACE: Heat1

Before a big race, participants often
compete in **heats**, which are preliminary
races that determine who competes in the
final race. Later, your class will compete in
a tricycle race against the winners of these
preliminary heats.

In the first heat, Leslie, Kristin, and Evie
rode tricycles toward the finish line. Leslie
started at the starting line and rode at a
constant rate of 2 meters every second. Kristin got an 8-meter head start and rode 2
meters every 5 seconds. Evie rode 5 meters every 4 seconds and got a 6-meter head
start.

a.   On neatly scaled axes, graph and write an equation in terms of x and y for the
distance Leslie travels. Let x represent time in seconds and y represent the
distance in meters. Then, do the same for Kristin and Evie using the same set of
axes.

b.   After how many seconds did Leslie catch up to Evie? How far were they from the
starting line when Leslie caught up to Evie? Confirm your answer algebraically.

c.   If the race is 20 meters long, who won? Use both the graph and the rules to
justify your answer.

Continued on next page→

7*63.   *Continued from previous page*

    d.   What is the slope of Kristin's line? How does her slope explain her rate of travel, also known as her speed?

    e.   Kaye also rode in this heat. When her distance line is graphed, the rule is $y = \frac{2}{3}x + 1$. What was her speed? Did she get a head start?

7*64.   TAKE A WALK

The President of the Line Factory is so impressed with your work that you have been given a special assignment: to analyze the graphs below, which were created when a customer walked in front of a motion detector. The motion detector recorded the distance between it and the customer.

Working with your team, explain what motion each graph below describes. In other words, how did the customer need to walk in order to create each graph? **Note:** Time is measured in 1-second increments along the *x*-axis, while distance from the detector is measured in 1-foot increments along the *y*-axis. Make sure you describe:

- if the customer was walking **toward** or **away** from the motion detector.
- where the customer began walking when the motion detector started collecting data.
- when the customer walked slowly and when he or she walked quickly.
- any time the customer changed direction or stopped.

a. 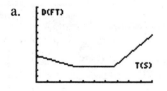   b. 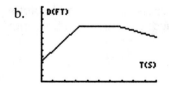   c.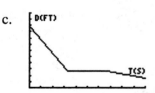

7*65.   OTHER RATES OF CHANGE

Problems 7*63 and 7*64 concentrated on situations where the slope of a line represented speed. However, we can graph many other situations that do not involve motion. Examine the graphs below and explain what real-world quantities the slope and y-intercepts represent. Find the slope and y-intercept. Write the measurement units with each of your answers (e.g., the slopes in problem 7*64 would be expressed in feet per second).

a.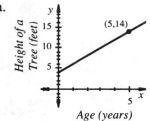
Age (years)

b.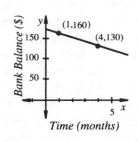
Time (months)

c.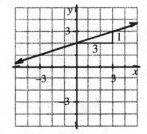
Gas (gallons)

METHODS AND MEANINGS

MATH NOTES

Writing the Equation of a Line from a Graph

One of the ways to write the equation of a line directly from a graph is to find the slope of the line (m) and the y-intercept (b). These values can then be substituted into the general slope-intercept form of a line: $y = mx + b$.

For example, the slope of the line at right is $m = \frac{1}{3}$, while the y-intercept is (0, 2). By substituting $m = \frac{1}{3}$ and $b = 2$ into $y = mx + b$, the equation of the line is:

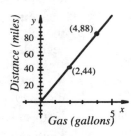

$$y = mx + b \quad \rightarrow \quad y = \tfrac{1}{3}x + 2$$

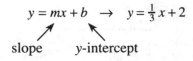

slope   y-intercept

7*66.   BIG RACE: Heat 2

Barbara, Elizabeth, and Carlos participated in the
second heat of The Big Race. Barbara thought
she could win with a 3-meter head start even
though she only peddled 3 meters every 2
seconds. Elizabeth started at the starting line and
finished the 20-meter race in 5 seconds.
Meanwhile, Carlos rode his tricycle so that his
distance (y) from the starting line in meters could
be represented by the rule $y = \frac{5}{2}x + 1$, where x
represents time in seconds.

a.   Using the given information, graph lines for Barbara, Elizabeth, and Carlos on the
same set of axes. Who won the 20-meter race and will advance to the final race?

b.   Find rules that describe Barbara's and Elizabeth's motion.

c.   How fast did Carlos peddle?

d.   When did Carlos pass Barbara? Confirm your answer algebraically.

7*67.   Salami and More Deli sells a 6-foot sandwich
for parties. It weighs 8 pounds. Assume the
weight per foot is constant.

a.   How much does a sandwich 0 feet long
weigh?

b.   Draw a graph showing the weight of the
sandwich (vertical axis) compared to the
length of the sandwich (horizontal axis).
Label the axes with appropriate units.

c.   Use your graph to estimate the weight of a 1-foot sandwich.

d.   Write a proportion to find the length of a 12-pound sandwich.

Algebra Connections: Chapter 7

7*68. Create a table and a graph for the line $y = 5x - 10$. Find the x-intercept and y-intercept in both the table and the graph.

7*69. Match the expressions in the left column with the equivalent expression on the right. Show and explain how you decided which ones matched.

a.	$(x + 5)(2x - 1)$	1.	$2x^2 + 9x - 5$
b.	$(2x - 5)(x + 1)$	2.	$2x^2 - 9x - 5$
c.	$(2x + 1)(x - 5)$	3.	$2x^2 - 3x - 5$

7*70. Complete the missing entries in the table below. Then write the rule.

IN (x)	2	10	6	7	-3		-10	100	x
OUT (y)	4	28	16			10			

7*71. Write and solve an equation (or system of equations) for the situation below. Define your variable(s) and write your solution as a sentence.

The Physical Education Department sells t-shirts for $12 and shorts for $8. One month, they sold 77 total items for $780 in total. How many t-shirts did they sell?

7.2.3 How can we use slope?

Rates of Change

Over the last four chapters you have found linear equations using many different strategies and starting from many different types of information. Today you are going to **apply** what you know about finding linear equations to solve a complicated puzzle: Who among you will win The Big Race?

7*72. THE BIG RACE: The Final Event

Today we will hold the final event of The Big Race. Your teacher will give you each a card that describes how you travel in the race. You and your study team will compete against Leslie and Elizabeth at today's rally in the gym.

Your task: As a team, do the following:

- Draw a graph showing all the racers' progress over time.

- Write an equation for each participant.

- Figure out who will win the race!

Rules:

- Your study team must work cooperatively to solve the problems. No team member has enough information to solve the puzzle alone!

- Each member of the team will select Rider A, B, C, or D. You may not show your card to your team. You may only communicate the information contained on the card.

- Assume that each racer travels at a constant rate throughout the race.

- Elizabeth's and Leslie's cards will be shared by the entire team.

7*73. Use your results from The Big Race to answer the following questions. You may deal with the questions in any order, but be sure to **justify** each response.

a. Who won The Big Race? Who came in last place?

b. How fast was Rider D traveling? How fast was Elizabeth traveling?

c. At one point in the race, four different participants were the same distance from the starting line. Who were they and when did this happen?

METHODS AND MEANINGS

x- and y-Intercepts

Recall that the **x-intercept** of a line is the point where the graph crosses the x-axis; that is, where $y = 0$. To find the x-intercept, substitute 0 for y and solve for x. The coordinates of the x-intercept are $(x, 0)$.

Similarly, the **y-intercept** of a line is the point where the graph crosses the y-axis, which happens when $x = 0$. To find the y-intercept, substitute 0 for x, and solve for y. The coordinates of the y-intercept are $(0, y)$.

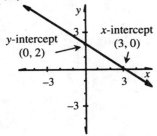

7*74. Find the point of intersection of these two lines:

$$3 = 6x - y$$
$$3x - 2y = 24$$

7*75. Sometimes the quickest and easiest two points to use to graph a line that is not in slope-intercept form are the x- and y-intercepts. Find the x- and y-intercepts for the two lines below and use them to graph each line. Write the coordinates of the x- and y-intercepts on your graph.

a. $x - 2y = 4$ b. $3x + 6y = 24$

7*76. Find the slope of the line passing through each pair of points below.

a. $(1, 2)$ and $(4, 5)$ b. $(7, 3)$ and $(5, 4)$

c. $(-6, 8)$ and $(-4, 5)$ d. $(55, 67)$ and $(50, 68)$

e. Azizah got 1 for the slope of the line through points $(1, 2)$ and $(4, -1)$. Explain to her the mistake she made and how to find the slope correctly.

7*77.   Simplify the following expressions.

   a. $15x^2 - 3x(4 + 5x)$ b. $\frac{1}{3}(24x - 9) + 10$

   c. $(x - 3)(x + 1) + 2x$ d. $6x - 2 + 9 - 3y - x$

7*78.   MATCH-A-GRAPH

   Match the following graphs with their equations. Pay special attention to the scaling of
   each set of axes. Explain how you found each match.

   1. $y = \frac{1}{4}x + 4$ 2. $y = \frac{1}{2}x + 4$

   3. $y = 2x + 4$ 4. $y = -\frac{2}{3}x + 4$

   a.   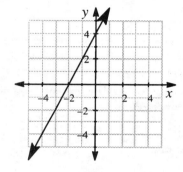   b.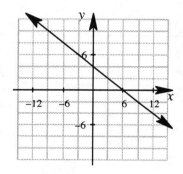

   c.   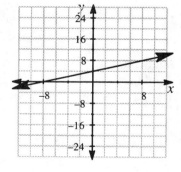   d.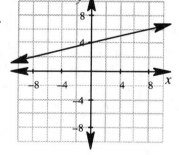

7*79.   **Multiple Choice:** The cost of a sweater is $3 less than the cost of a pair of jeans, while
   a hat is twice the cost of a sweater. If the pair of jeans costs j dollars, then which
   expression below represents the cost of the hat?

   a. $2j$ b. $j - 3$ c. $2(j - 3)$ d. $2j - 3$

7.3.1 How can we find the equation?

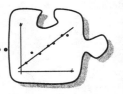

Finding an Equation Given a Slope and a Point

To do well in the Big Race activity, you had to find the equation of a line with a given rate (slope) that passed through a given point. Your method probably involved estimating the y-intercept of the line visually or working backward on a graph. What if the given point is far away from the y-axis? What if an estimate is not good enough in a particular situation?

During this lesson, you will develop an algebraic method for finding the equation of a line when given its slope and a point on the line.

7*80.   DOWN ON THE FARM

Colleen recently purchased a farm that raises chickens. Since she has never raised chickens before, Colleen wants to learn as much about her new brood of chickens as possible. In particular, she wants to know how much a baby chick weighs when it is hatched.

To find out, Colleen decided to track the weight of one of the chickens that was born just before she purchased the farm. She found that her chick grew steadily by about 5.2 grams each day, and she assumes that it has been doing so since it hatched. Nine days after it hatched, the chick weighed 98.4 grams.

Your task: Determine how much the chick weighed the day it was hatched using two different representations of the chick's growth: a graph and an $x \rightarrow y$ table. Then, assuming the chicken will continue to grow at the same rate, determine when the chick will weigh 140 grams.

Discussion Points

What are you looking for?

What information are you given?

What do you expect the graph to look like? Why?

Which representation (graph or table) will give more accurate results? Why?

7*81.   USING A GRAPH

Use the information in problem 7*80 to answer these questions.

a.   What is the baby chick's rate of growth? That is, how fast does the baby chick grow? How does this rate relate to the equation of the line?

b.   Before graphing, describe the line that represents the growth of the chicken. Do you know any points on the line? Does the line point upward or downward? How steep is it?

c.   Draw a graph for this situation. Let the horizontal axis represent the number of days since the chick hatched, and let the vertical axis represent the chick's weight. Label and scale your axes appropriately and title your graph "Growth of a Baby Chick."

d.   What is the *y*-intercept of your graph? According to your graph, how much did Colleen's chick weigh the day it hatched?

e.   When will the chick weigh 140 grams?

7*82.   USING A TABLE

Use the information in problem 7*80 to answer these questions.

a.   Now approach this problem using a table. Make a table with two columns, the first labeled "Days Since Birth" and the second labeled "Weight in Grams." In the first column, write the numbers 0 through 10.

b.   Use Colleen's measurements to fill one entry in the table.

c.   Use the chick's growth rate to complete the table.

d.   According to your table, how much did the chick weigh the day it was hatched? When will the chick weigh 140 grams? Do these answers match your answers from the graph? Which method do you think is more accurate? Why?

7*83.   FINDING AN EQUATION WITHOUT A TABLE OR GRAPH

Now you will explore another way Colleen could find the weight of her chick when it hatched without using a table or a graph.

a.   Since Colleen is assuming the chick grows linearly, the equation will be in the form $y = mx + b$. Without graphing, what do m and b represent? Do we know either of these values?

b.   You already know the chicken's rate of growth. Place the slope into the equation of the line. What information is still unknown?

c.   In Lesson 7.1.4, you discovered that knowing the slope and a point **is** enough information to determine a line. Therefore, using the point (9, 98.4) should help us find the y-intercept. How can we use this point in our equation? Discuss this with your team and be ready to share your ideas with the rest of the class.

d.   Work together as a class to solve for b, that is, the weight of the chick when it was hatched.

e.   Write the equation of the line that represents the weight of the chick.

f.   Does the y-intercept you found algebraically match the one you found using the graph? Does it match the one you found using the table? How accurate do you think your algebraic answer is?

g.   Use your equation to determine when Colleen's chicken will weigh 140 grams.

h.   Of the graphical, table, and algebraic methods, which do you prefer? With your team, list some advantages and disadvantages of each method. Can you think of a situation that would make it difficult to use some of the methods?

7*84.   Use this new algebraic method to find equations for lines with the following properties:

a.   A slope of -3, passing through the point (15, -50).

b.   A slope of 0.5, with an x-intercept of 28.

7*85.   Today we used $y = mx + b$ in yet another way. As a Learning Reflection, explain how you can find the equation of a line knowing only the slope and one point on the line.

7*86.   EXTENSION

The earth's surface is composed of gigantic
plates that are constantly moving.
Currently, India lies on a plate that is
slowly drifting northward, grinding into the
rest of Asia. As it does so, it pushes up the
Himalayan mountains, which contain the
world's highest peak, Mt. Everest. In 1999,
Mt. Everest was measured by mountain
climbers with satellite gear to be 8,850 meters high. Geologists estimate that Mt.
Everest may be growing by as much as 5 cm per year.

Your task: Assuming a constant growth of 5 cm per year, determine how tall Mt.
Everest was in the year 0. (The year 0 is the year that came 2000 years before the year
2000.) Write an equation for the height of Mt. Everest over time, with x representing
the year and y representing the height of the mountain.

7*87.   The point (21, 32) is on a line with slope 1.5.

a.   Find the equation of the line.

b.   Find the coordinates of a third point on the line.

7*88.   Complete the following Diamond Problems. Remember that the product goes on the
top and the sum on the bottom.

a.   b.   c.   d.

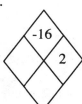   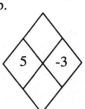   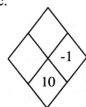   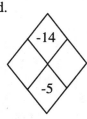

7*89.   Solve the following systems of equations. Remember to check your solution in both equations to make sure it is the point of intersection.

a. $y = 2x - 3$
      $x - y = -4$

b. $y - x = -2$
      $-3y + 2x = 14$

7*90.   Solve each of the following equations for x.

a. $\frac{x}{6} = \frac{7}{3}$

b. $3x + 2 = 7x - 8$

c. $\frac{6}{x} = \frac{4}{x+1}$

d. $6(x - 4) = 42$

7*91.   The graph of the equation $2x - 3y = 7$ is a line.

a.   Find the x- and y-intercepts and graph the line using these two points.

b.   If a point on this line has an x-coordinate of 10, what is its y-coordinate?

7*92.   Without graphing, identify the slope and y-intercept of the following equations:

a. $y = 3x + 5$

b. $y = \frac{5}{-4} x$

c. $y = 3$

d. $y = 7 + 4x$

e. $3x + 4y = -4$

f. $x + 5y = 30$

7.3.2 What if the lines are perpendicular?

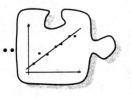

Slopes of Parallel and Perpendicular Lines

In Lesson 7.1.5, you found that the slopes of parallel lines are equal because lines with the same steepness grow at the same rate. What about the slopes of perpendicular lines (lines that form a right angle)? Today you will answer this question and then use parallel and perpendicular lines to find the equations of other lines.

7*93.   SLOPES OF PERPENDICULAR LINES

Draw a square on your paper.

a.   What do you know about the opposite sides of a square? What about adjacent
      sides (sides next to each other that form a corner of the square)?

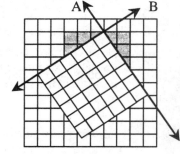

b.   A six-by-six square was rotated and placed on
      the grid, as shown at right. Lines A and B are
      formed by the edges of the square. Find the
      slope of the two perpendicular lines, A and B,
      using the shaded slope triangles.

c.   Based on this example, how do the slopes of
      perpendicular lines seem to be related? How are
      they different? In other words, if you have two
      perpendicular lines, how can you get the slope
      of one from the other?

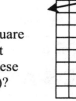

d.   To test her observation, Cheryl rotated the square
      differently to form lines C and D, as shown at
      right. Find the slope of lines C and D. Do these
      slopes confirm your observation from part (c)?

e.   Do you think your observation from part (c) above is always true? Are the two
      slope triangles of perpendicular lines always related in this manner? Obtain the
      resource page and scissors from your teacher. Carefully cut out the 6-by-6 square
      on your Resource Page and test your theory on the grid using at least three
      different pairs of perpendicular lines. Discuss this with your teammates and be
      ready to share your ideas with the class.

f.   What about the slopes of parallel lines? How are they related? Test your theory
      using the 6-by-6 square on the grid.

7*94.   Use what you discovered about the slopes of parallel and perpendicular lines to find the
         equation of each line described below.

a.   Find the equation of the line that goes through the point (2, -3) and is
      perpendicular to the line $y = -\frac{2}{5}x + 6$.

b.   Find the equation of the line that is parallel to the line $-3x + 2y = 10$ and that
      goes through the point (4, 7).

7*95.   Line L is perpendicular to the line $6x - y = 7$ and passes through the point $(0, 6)$. Line M is parallel to the line $y = \frac{2}{3}x - 4$ and passes through the point $(-3, -1)$. Where do these lines intersect? Explain how you found your solution.

7*96.   EXTENSION

Suppose the rule for line A is $y = \frac{6}{5}x - 10$. Line A is parallel to line B, which is perpendicular to line C. If line D is perpendicular to line C and perpendicular to line E, what is the slope of line E? **Justify** your conclusion.

7*97.   As a Learning Reflection, summarize what you have learned today. Be sure to explain the relationship of the slopes of perpendicular lines and describe how to get the slope of one line when you know the slope of a line perpendicular to it. Title this entry, "Slopes of Perpendicular Lines" and include today's date.

⊕ETHODS AND MEANINGS

Parallel and Perpendicular Lines

Parallel lines lie in the same plane (a flat surface) and never intersect. They have the same steepness, and therefore they grow at the same rate. Lines l and n at right are examples of parallel lines.

On the other hand, **perpendicular lines** are lines that intersect at a right angle. For example, lines m and n at right are perpendicular, as are lines m and l. Note that the small square drawn at the point of intersection indicates a right angle.

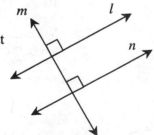

The **slopes of parallel lines** are the same. In general, the slope of a line parallel to a line with slope m is m.

The **slopes of perpendicular lines** are opposite reciprocals. For example, if one line has slope $\frac{4}{5}$, then any line perpendicular to it has slope $-\frac{5}{4}$. If a line has slope -3, then any line perpendicular to it has slope $\frac{1}{3}$. In general, the slope of a line perpendicular to a line with slope m is $-\frac{1}{m}$.

7*98. Dean and Carlos decided to hold their own race. Dean estimates that he rides 3 meters every 4 seconds and wants a 5-meter head start. Carlos will ride 1 meter per second.

a. How many meters does Dean ride each second?

b. On one set of axes, graph and label lines to represent each rider's distance from the starting line. Find the equation for each rider.

c. Use the equations you wrote to determine when Carlos and Dean will be the same distance from the starting line.

7*99. Explain what the slope of each line below represents. Then find the slope.

a.

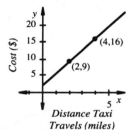

Distance Taxi Travels (miles)

b.

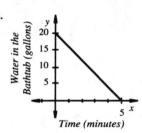

Time (minutes)

7*100. Which of the triangles below is similar to triangle ABC at right? For each figure, explain how you know.

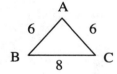

a.

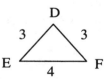

b.

7*101. Find the x-intercepts of the parabola $y = x^2 + 2x - 15$ using any representation you want. Then explain your method.

7*102. Find the following products.

a. $(2x - 1)(x + 3)$

b. $3x(5x - 11)$

c. $(x - 5)(5x - 2)$

d. $100(3x - 0.5)$

7*103. **Multiple Choice:** What is the slope of the line through the points (-7, 10) and (1, 4)?

a. $\frac{3}{4}$

b. $-\frac{3}{4}$

c. 1

d. -1

7.3.3 What if we only have two points?

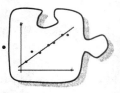

Finding the Equation of a Line through Two Points

So far, you know how to find the equation of a line with a given slope and a *y*-intercept or other point on the line. You have developed tools that help you find the equation using either a graph, a table, or an algebraic process. Today you are going to expand your set of tools to include finding an equation of a line through two points. As you work on today's problems, keep these questions in mind:

What do you know about the line?

How can you use that information to find the equation?

How can you verify that your equation is correct?

7*104. Without graphing, find the equation of the line through the points (14, 52) and (29, 97). Use the questions below to help you organize your work.

    a. What is the slope of the line?

    b. How can you use a point to find the equation? Find the equation of the line.

    c. Once you have the slope, does it matter which point you use to find your equation?

    d. How can you verify that your equation is correct?

7*105. As a Learning Reflection, describe the process you used in problem 7*104 to find the equation of a line through two points without graphing. Include an example. Title this entry, "How to Find the Equation of a Line Through Two Points" and include today's date.

7*106.   WELCOME TO DISNEYLAND!

Finding the equation of a line between two points can be an effective method for finding trend lines for data. Trend lines represent linear data and can be used to make predictions about an event or situation. In this problem, the process you used in problem 7*104 will help us make a prediction.

For over 50 years, Disneyland has kept track of how many guests pass through its entrance gates. Below is a table with the names and dates of some significant guests. Predict when the 1 billionth guest will pass through Disneyland's gates.

Name	Year	Guest
Elsa Marquez	1955	1 millionth guest
Leigh Woolfenden	1957	10 millionth guest
Dr. Glenn C. Franklin	1961	25 millionth guest
Mary Adams	1965	50 millionth guest
Valerie Suldo	1971	100 millionth guest
Gert Schelvis	1981	200 millionth guest
Brook Charles Arthur Burr	1985	250 millionth guest
Claudine Masson	1989	300 millionth guest
Minnie Pepito	1997	400 millionth guest
Mark Ramirez	2001	450 millionth guest

a.   With your team, represent the data on your grapher or on graph paper. Let $x = 1955$ to represent the year 1955.

b.   Select two points from the data that will make a good trend line. You should choose your points so that when they are connected by a line, that line will pass through the middle of all the data and will resemble the overall trend of the data. Every member of your team should use the same two points. Be prepared to explain your choice of points and your solution to the class.

c.   Use the two points you chose to find an equation for your trend line. Show your algebraic thinking.

d.   Graph your line on the same axes as your data (either on your graph paper or on your grapher). Does your line pass through the two points you chose? If not, go back and check your work. Does the equation seem to do a good job of fitting the data?

Continued on next page →

Algebra Connections: Chapter 7

7*106.   *Continued from previous page*

     e.   What is the *y*-intercept of your line? Why does it make sense that it is negative?

     f.   Use your equation to make a prediction: If you want to be Disneyland's 1 billionth guest, during what year should you go to the park? Remember that 1 billion is 1,000 millions.

METHODS AND MEANINGS

MATH NOTES

Trend Lines

A **trend line** is a line that represents a set of data. It does not need to intersect each data point. Rather, it needs to approximate the data. A trend line looks and "behaves" like the data, as shown in the example at right.

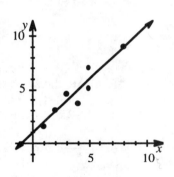

Review & Preview

7*107.   Find the equations of the lines described below.

     a.   The line parallel to the line $y = \frac{1}{5}x - 6$ that goes through the point (-5, 3).

     b.   The line that goes through the points (100, 76) and (106, 58).

7*108. Find the point of intersection of the system of linear equations below.

$$8 - 3x = y$$
$$2y + 3x = 5$$

7*109. On graph paper, graph the parabola $y = x^2 - 6x + 10$.

    a. Label the x- and y-intercepts, if possible.

    b. The highest or lowest point on a parabola is called the **vertex**. What is the vertex of this parabola?

7*110. Evaluate the expressions below for the given values.

    a. $-2x^2 - 3x + 1$ for $x = -3$ b. $8 - (3x - 2)^2$ for $x = -2$

    c. $\frac{-3}{k+2}$ for $k = -3$ d. $\frac{15m}{n+1} - m^2 + n$ for $m = 1, n = 2$

7*111. Of the eight lines below, which are perpendicular? Which are parallel? How do you know?

    a. $y = \frac{-5}{6}x + 3$ b. $y = 3$ c. $5x + 6y = 9$ d. $x = -4$

    e. $y = -4x - 5$ f. $y = \frac{1}{4}x - 7$ g. $4x - y = 2$ h. $y = 5 - \frac{6}{5}x$

7*112. Find the equation of the line with x-intercept (-4, 0) and y-intercept (0, 9).

7.3.4 What is the equation of the line?

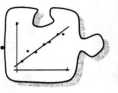

Finding Linear Equations Given Graphs

In past lessons, we learned facts about m and b by graphing lines from rules. In today's lesson, we will **reverse** the process used in Lesson 7.1.1 so that we can find the equation of a line when we know its graph.

7*113.　LINE FACTORY LOGO

The Line Factory needs a new logo for its pamphlet. After much work by the design staff, the two logos shown below were proposed.

The only problem is that the staff clerks need to have the equations of the lines in each design to program their pamphlet production software.

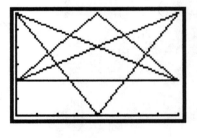

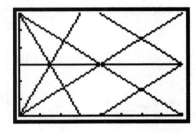

Logo A　　　　　　　　　　　　　Logo B

Your Task: Your team needs to find the equations of the lines in Logos A and B and recreate the graphs on your calculators. Split your team into two pairs so that one pair will work on Logo A while the other works on Logo B.

Find the equations of the lines in your design and then use your grapher to check them. Assume that the axes above are scaled by ones and be sure to set your window as shown at right so that the x-axis contains the values between 0 and 8 and the y-axis contains the values between 0 and 6. Once you have found all the equations, draw all the lines simultaneously on the same set of axes to recreate the logo on your grapher.

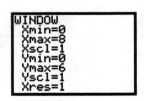

Discussion Points

How many equations should you have for each logo?

What is different about some of the lines? What is the same?

How can you find the equation of a line from its graph?

MATH NOTES

METHODS AND MEANINGS

Point-Slope Form of a Line

Another method for finding the equation of a line when given its slope and a point on the line uses the *point-slope* form of a line. This form is:

$$y - k = m(x - h)$$

where (h, k) is a point on the line and m is the slope. For example, to find the equation of the line with slope $m = -3$ through the point (6, 1), substitute these values into $y - k = m(x - h)$ as shown below:

$$y - 1 = -3(x - 6)$$

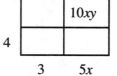

This result can then be changed to $y = mx + b$ form:

$$y - 1 = -3(x - 6)$$
$$y - 1 = -3x + 18$$
$$y = -3x + 19$$

Thus, the equation of the line with slope $m = -3$ through the point (6, 1) can be written as $y - 1 = -3(x - 6)$ or $y = -3x + 19$.

7*114.   Complete each generic rectangle below and write the area as a sum and a product.

a.
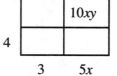

b.
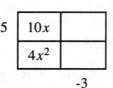

7*115.   Peggy decided to sell brownies and cookies to raise
          money for her basketball uniform. She sold brownies
          for $3.00 and cookies for $2.50. If she sold 3 fewer
          cookies than brownies and collected $218 in total,
          then how many brownies did she sell?

7*116.   Find the equation of each line below.

          a.   The line with slope $m = \frac{-2}{3}$ through the point (-6, 5).

          b.   A horizontal line through the point (8, -11).

          c.   The line perpendicular to the line in part (a) above but through the origin.

7*117.   Explain what the slope of each line below represents. Then find the slope.

          a.   b.

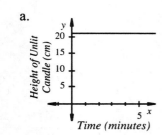

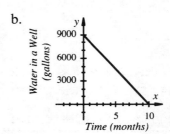

7*118.   Complete the following Diamond Problems. Remember that the product goes on the
          top and the sum on the bottom.

          a.   b.   c.   d.

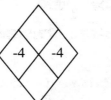

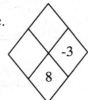

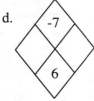

7*119.   Simplify.

          a. $5x(3x)$ b. $5x + 3x$

          c. $6x(x)$ d. $6x + x$

① TEAM BRAINSTORM

> With your team, brainstorm a list for each of the following topics. Be as detailed as you can. How long can you make your list? Challenge yourselves.

> **Topics:**   What have we studied in this chapter? What ideas and words were important in what we learned? Remember to be as detailed as you can.

> **Ways of Thinking:**   What ways of thinking have we used in this chapter? When did we use them?

> **Connections:**   What topics, ideas, and words we learned *before* this chapter are connected to the new ideas in this chapter? Again, make your list as long as you can.

> Be prepared to share your team's ideas with the class.

② MAKING CONNECTIONS

> The following is a list of all of the key words in this chapter. The words that appear in bold are new to this chapter. Make sure that you are familiar with all of these words.

coordinates	graph	growth
linear equation	parallel	**steepness (p. 278, 280)**
perpendicular (p. 307)	prediction	solution
rate of change (p. 288)	**slope (p. 278, 280, 288)**	$y = mx + b$
slope triangle (p. 278, 280)	x-intercept	**Δx (p. 278, 280)**
trend line (p. 311)	y-intercept	**Δy (p. 278, 280)**

> Make a concept map showing all of the **connections** you can find between the key words and ideas listed above. For each key word or idea, sketch an example. Label each connection with a phrase explaining how the ideas are related. While you are making your map, you may think of related ideas that are not listed above. Be sure to include these ideas in your concept map.

③ SUMMARIZING MY UNDERSTANDING

This section gives you an opportunity to show what you know about one or more topics or ideas. Your teacher will give you directions for exactly how to do this.

④ WHERE AM I?

This section will help you evaluate which types of problems you have seen you feel comfortable with and which you need more help with. This section appears at the end of every chapter to help you check your understanding. Even if your teacher does not assign this section, it is a good idea to try the problems and find out for yourself what you know and what you need to work on.

Solve each problem as completely as you can. The table at the end of the closure section has answers to these problems. It also tells you where you can find additional help and practice on problems like these.

CL 7*1.   For the line graphed at right:

    a.   find the slope.

    b.   find the y-intercept.

    c.   write the equation.

    d.   find the equation of a parallel line that passes through $(0, 7)$.

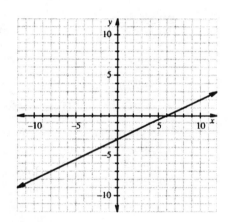

CL 7*2.   Find m and b in the following equations. (You will have to put some in $y = mx + b$ form first.)

    a. $y = 2x + 1$ b. $y = \frac{2}{5}x - 4$

    c. $2x + y = 15$ d. $3x + 2y = 4$

CL 7*3.   For each system of equations, find the point of intersection.

    a. $3x + 4y = 25$
         $y = x + 1$

    b. $5x - 2y = 23$
         $-4x + 2y = -18$

CL 7*4. Shirley starts with $85 in the bank and saves $15 every 2 months. Joshua starts with $212.50 and spends $20 every 3 months.

     a. Write equations for the balances of Shirley's and Joshua's bank accounts.

     b. When will Shirley and Joshua have the same amount of money? How much money will they have then?

CL 7*5. Shannon wants to estimate how many people live in her neighborhood. She knows that there are 56 houses on four blocks and there are 62 blocks in her neighborhood.

     a. How many houses are in her neighborhood?

     b. Shannon estimates that on average 4 people live in each house. About how many people live in her neighborhood?

CL 7*6. Louis and Max are contestants in a jellybean-eating contest. Louis eats 18 jelly beans in 30 seconds. Max eats 24 jellybeans in 40 seconds.

     a. Who is eating jellybeans faster?

     b. Because Max has also been in a pie-eating contest today, he gets a 5 jellybean head start. If the contest lasts 3 minutes (180 seconds), who will win?

CL 7*7. Solve for m: $6m - 5 + 8m - (2m + 3) = 3(3m - 8)$.

CL 7*8. Match each equation to the situation and its graph. Explain how you know that all three go together.

Situations for each person	Equations	Graphs
1. Has $5 after 6 days	i. $x + 2y = 18$	
2. Has nothing after 7 days	ii. $y = \frac{2}{3}x + 1$	
3. Has $9 after 1 day	iii. $2x + 6y = 90$	
4. Has $10 after 2 days	iv. $y = 4x + 5$	
5. Started with $15	v. $y = -x + 7$	

CL 7*9.   Write the area of each rectangle as a product and a sum.

a.

b.

CL 7*10.   For each equation below, write the equation of a line that is **parallel** to the given line and another that is **perpendicular** to it.

a. $y = \frac{4}{3}x - 7$ b. $y = 5x - 1$ c. $y = -2x + 1$

CL 7*11.   Make a table and graph $y = x^2 - 3x - 10$.

CL 7*12.   Glenn sells packets of transit tickets for the city. A cable car ticket costs $3, a bus ticket costs $1, and a subway ticket costs $2. Each packet Glenn sells has 4 bus tickets, 2 subway tickets, and 1 cable car ticket. If Glenn sold $418 of tickets today, how many of each type of ticket did he sell?

CL 7*13.   Here are four equations of lines:

i. $y = 6$ ii. $y = 8 - x$

iii. $y = -x - 7$ iv. $y = x + 1$

a.   Are any of these lines parallel? How can you tell?

b.   Are any of these lines perpendicular? How can you tell?

c.   Graph all four lines on the same axes.

d.   Record the x- and y-intercepts for each line.

CL 7*14.   Find the equation of the line that passes through the points $(-5, 7)$ and $(10, 1)$.

CL 7*15.   Check your answers to each problem above using the table at the end of the closure section. Which problems did you feel confident about? Which problems were hard? Use the table to make a list of topics you need help on and a list of topics you need to practice more.

⑤ HOW AM I THINKING?

This course emphasizes the following five ways of thinking:

- Reversing processes (going in both directions)
- Justifying (explaining why)
- Generalizing (showing how it works for all cases)
- Making Connections (showing how it fits in with other ideas)
- Applying and/or extending our knowledge (thinking about how we use it or where it can go)

Choose three of these ways of thinking that you remember using while working in this chapter. For each way of thinking that you choose, show and explain where you used it and how you used it. Describe why thinking in this way helped you solve a particular problem or understand something new. (For instance, explain why we wanted to generalize in this particular case, or why it was useful to see these particular connections.) Be sure to include examples to demonstrate your thinking.

Problem	Solution	Need Help?	More Practice
CL 7*1	a. The slope is $\frac{1}{2}$. b. The y-intercept is -3. c. $y = \frac{1}{2}x - 3$ d. $y = \frac{1}{2}x + 7$	MN p. 288, MN p. 295, MN p. 299, MN p. 307	7*21, 7*23, 7*24, 7*25, 7*33, 7*35, 7*47, 7*50, 7*57, 7*62, 7*66, 7*98, 7*116
CL 7*2	a. $m = 2, b = 1$ b. $m = \frac{2}{5}, b = -4$ c. $m = -2, b = 15$ d. $m = -\frac{3}{2}, b = 2$	MN p. 199, MN p. 288, MN p. 295	7*32, 7*34, 7*43, 7*44, 7*92
CL 7*3	a. $(3,4)$ b. $(5,1)$	MN p. 271	7*5, 7*27, 7*39, 7*49, 7*60, 7*74, 7*89, 7*95, 7*108

Problem	Solution	Need Help?	More Practice
CL 7*4	a. Let x = the # of months that have passed Let y = the amount of money in the account For Shirley: $y = \frac{15}{2}x + 85$ For Joshua: $y = -\frac{20}{3}x + 212.5$ b. They will have the same amount of money after 9 months. They will each have \$152.50 in their accounts.	MN p. 244, MN p. 271	7*5, 7*39, 7*48, 7*59, 7*63, 7*66, 7*89, 7*98
CL 7*5	a. There are 868 houses in the neighborhood. b. There are 3472 people in the neighborhood.	MN p. 206	7*7, 7*17, 7*42, 7*58, 7*67, 7*100
CL 7*6	a. They are eating jellybeans at the same rate (36 jellybeans per minute). b. Max will win. After 3 minutes, Louis will have eaten 108 jellybeans and Max will have eaten 113 jellybeans.	MN p. 280	7*19, 7*65, 7*99
CL 7*7	$m = -\frac{16}{3}$	MN p. 202, Section 6.2	7*8, 7*16, 7*29, 7*40, 7*51, 7*52, 7*89
CL 7*8	Situation 1, Equation *ii*, Graph *c* because the point (6,5) lies on the graph and satisfies the equation. Situation 2, Equation *v*, Graph *e* because the *x*-intercept is at (0,7). Situation 3, Equation *iv*, Graph *a* because the point (1,9) lies on the graph and satisfies the equation. Situation 4, Equation *i*, Graph *b* because the point (2,10) lies on the graph and satisfies the equation. Situation 5, Equation *iii*, Graph *d* because the *y*-intercept is 15.	MN p. 295, MN p. 299	7*38, 7*44, 7*64, 7*65, 7*78

Problem	Solution	Need Help?	More Practice

CL 7*9   a.

$$\begin{array}{c|c|c}
 & x & +\ 3 \\
\hline
2x & 2x^2 & 6x \\
\hline
-5 & -5x & -15 \\
\end{array}$$

$2x^2 + x - 15$

MN p. 213

7*31, 7*41,
7*61, 7*69,
7*77, 7*102,
7*114

b.

$$\begin{array}{c|c|c}
 & x & -\ 4 \\
\hline
3x & 3x^2 & -12x \\
\hline
-6 & -6x & 24 \\
\end{array}$$

$3x^2 - 18x + 24$

CL 7*10   a. parallel: $y = \frac{4}{3}x - 2$

perpendicular: $y = -\frac{3}{4}x + 3$

b. parallel: $y = 5x + 4$

perpendicular: $y = -\frac{1}{5}x + 4$

c. parallel: $y = -2x - 2$

perpendicular: $y = \frac{1}{2}x + 5$

MN p. 307

7*38, 7*45,
7*94, 7*95,
7*107, 7*111,
7*116

CL 7*11

x	-2	-1	0	1	2	3	4	5	6	7	8
y	0	-6	-10	-12	-12	-10	-8	0	8	18	30

Section 4.1

7*26, 7*68,
7*70, 7*78,
7*82, 7*109

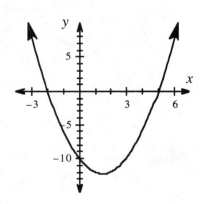

Problem	Solution	Need Help?	More Practice
CL 7*12	Glen sold 152 bus tickets, 76 subway tickets, and 38 cable car tickets.	MN p.228, 6*3, 6*5	7*9, 7*18, 7*30, 7*48, 7*71, 7*79, 7*115
CL 7*13	a. Lines *ii* and *iii* are parallel. Each has a slope of -1. b. Line *iv* is perpendicular to lines *ii* and *iii*. The slopes (1 and -1) are opposite reciprocals. c. d. line *i*: *x*-int does not exist, *y*-int 6 line *ii*: *x*-int 8, *y*-int 8 line *iii*: *x*-int -7, *y*-int -7 line *iv*: *x*-int -1, *y*-int 1	MN p. 299, MN p. 307	7*6, 7*28, 7*45, 7*53, 7*68, 7*75, 7*91, 7*94, 7*95, 7*101, 7*107, 7*109, 7*112
CL 7*14	$y = -\frac{2}{5}x + 5$	MN p. 288, MN p. 314	7*44, 7*62, 7*76, 7*84, 7*87, 7*91, 7*103, 7*104, 7*107, 7*116

CHAPTER 8

In Chapter 4 you used a web to find the connections between each of the different representations of lines. This empowered you to use any representation (such as a graph, rule, situation or table) to find any of the other representations.

In this chapter a quadratics web will challenge us to find connections between the different representations of a parabola. Through this endeavor, you will learn how to rewrite quadratic equations by using a process called factoring. Finally, you will discover a very important property of zero.

In this chapter, you will learn:

➢ How to factor a quadratic expression completely.

➢ How to find the roots (*x*-intercepts) of a quadratic equation, if they exist.

➢ How to move from all representations (line, graph, table, and situation) of a parabola to each of the other representations.

➢ How to distinguish between intercepts and intersections.

Guiding Questions

Think about these questions throughout this chapter:

How can I rewrite it?

What's the connection?

What is special about zero?

What information do I need?

Is there another method?

Chapter Outline

Section 8.1   In this section, you will develop a method to change a quadratic equation written as a sum into its product form (also called its factored form).

Section 8.2   Through a fun application, you will find ways to generate each representation of a parabola from each of the others. You will also develop a method to solve quadratic equations using the Zero Product Property.

Section 8.3   In this section, you will be introduced to another method to solve quadratic equations called the Quadratic Formula.

8.1.1 How can we find the product?

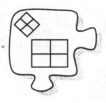

Introduction to Factoring Quadratics

In Chapter 5 you learned how to multiply algebraic expressions using algebra tiles and generic rectangles. This section will focus on reversing this process: how can we find a product when given a sum?

8*1.   Review what you know about products and sums below.

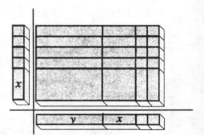

   a.   Write the area of the rectangle at right as a product and a sum. Remember that the product represents the area found by multiplying (length)(width), while the sum is the sum of the areas inside the rectangle.

   b.   Use a generic rectangle to multiply $(6x-1)(3x+2)$. Write your solution as a sum.

8*2.   The process of changing a sum to a product is called **factoring**. Can every expression be factored? That is, *does every sum have a product that can be represented with tiles?*

   Investigate this question by building rectangles using algebra tiles for the following expressions. For each one, write the area as a sum and as a product. If you cannot find a rectangle, be prepared to convince the class that no rectangle exists (and thus the expression cannot be factored).

   a. $2x^2 + 7x + 6$ b. $6x^2 + 7x + 2$

   c. $x^2 + 4x + 1$ d. $2xy + 6x + y^2 + 3y$

8*3.   Work with your team to find the sum and product for the following generic rectangles. Are there any special strategies you discovered that can help determine the dimensions of the rectangle? Be sure to share these strategies with your teammates.

a.

$2x$	5
$6x^2$	$15x$

b.

$-2y$	-6
$5xy$	$15x$

c.

$-9x$	-12
$12x^2$	$16x$

d.

$2x$	-12
$4x^2$	$-24x$

8*4.   While working on problem 8*3, Casey noticed a pattern with the diagonals of each generic rectangle. However, just before she shared her pattern with the rest of her team, she was called out of class! The drawing on her paper looked like the diagram below. Can you figure out what the two diagonals have in common?

$2x$	5
$6x^2$	$15x$

8*5.   Does Casey's pattern always work? Verify that her pattern works for all of the 2 x 2 generic rectangles in problem 8*3. Then describe Casey's pattern for the diagonals of a 2 x 2 generic rectangle as a Learning Reflection. Be sure to include an example. Title this entry "Diagonals of a Generic Rectangle" and include today's date.

METHODS AND MEANINGS

MATH NOTES

New Vocabulary to Describe Algebraic Expressions

Since algebraic expressions come in many different forms, we have special words to help us describe these expressions. For example, if the equation can be written in the form $ax^2 + bx + c = 0$ and if a is not 0, it is called a **quadratic** expression. Study the examples of quadratic expressions below.

Examples of quadratic expressions: $x^2 - 15x + 26$,
$16m^2 - 25$, and $12 - 3k^2 + 5k$

The way an expression is written can also be described. When an expression is written in product-form, it is described as being **factored**. When factored, each of the expressions being multiplied is called a **factor**. For example, the factored form of $x^2 - 15x + 26$ is $(x - 13)(x - 2)$, so $x - 13$ and $x - 2$ are each factors of the original expression.

Finally, the number of terms in an expression can help us describe the expression to others. If the expression has one term, it is called a **monomial**, while an expression with two terms is called a **binomial**. If the expression has three terms, it is called a **trinomial**. Study the examples below.

Examples of monomials: $15xy^2$ and $-2m$

Examples of binomials: $16m^2 - 25$ and $7h^9 + \frac{1}{2}h$

Examples of trinomials: $12 - 3k^2 + 5k$ and $x^2 - 15x + 26$

$2x^2$	$4xy$	$-8x$
$-3x$	$-6y$	12

8*6.   Write the area at right as a sum and as a product.

8*7.   Multiply the expressions below using a generic rectangle. Then verify Casey's pattern (that the product of one diagonal equals the product of the other diagonal).

    a. $(4x-1)(3x+5)$ b. $(2x-7)^2$

8*8.   Remember that a Diamond Problem is a pattern for which the **product** of two numbers is placed on top, while the **sum** of the same two numbers is placed on bottom. Study the example at right and then complete the diamond problems below.

Product

Sum

    a.   b.   c.

    d.   e.   f.

8*9.   For each line below, name the slope and y-intercept.

    a. $y = \frac{-1+4x}{2}$ b. $3x+y=-7$ c. $y=\frac{-2}{3}x+8$ d. $y=-2$

8*10.   On graph paper, graph $y = x^2 - 2x - 8$.

    a.   Name the y-intercept. What is the **connection** between the y-intercept and the rule $f(x) = x^2 - 2x - 8$?

    b.   Name the x-intercepts.

    c.   Find the lowest point of the graph, the vertex.

8*11.   Calculate these expressions.

    a. $5 - \sqrt{36}$ b. $1 + \sqrt{39}$ c. $-2 - \sqrt{5}$

8.1.2 Is there a shortcut?

· ·

Factoring with Generic Rectangles

Since mathematics is often described as the study of patterns, it is not surprising that generic rectangles have many patterns. You saw one important pattern in Lesson 8.1.1 (Casey's pattern from problem 8*4). Today you will continue to use patterns while you develop a method to factor trinomial expressions.

$-35x$	14
$10x^2$	$-4x$

8*12.   Examine the generic rectangle shown at right.

    a.   Review what you learned in Lesson 8.1.1 by writing the area of the rectangle at right as a sum and as a product.

    b.   Does this generic rectangle fit Casey's pattern for diagonals? Demonstrate that the product of each diagonal is equal.

8*13.   FACTORING QUADRATICS

    In order to develop a method to factor without using algebra tiles, first study how to factor with algebra tiles, then look for **connections** within a generic rectangle.

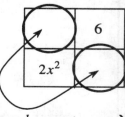

    a.   Using algebra tiles, factor $2x^2 + 5x + 3$; that is, use the tiles to build a rectangle and then write its area as a product.

    b.   Factoring with tiles (like you did in part (a)) is easy because you can try many different arrangements of tiles and can visually check to see if they form a rectangle. Using a generic rectangle to factor requires a different process.

        Miguel wants to use a generic rectangle to factor $3x^2 + 10x + 8$. He knows that $3x^2$ and 8 go into the rectangle in the locations shown at right. Finish the rectangle by deciding how to place the 10 x-terms. Then write the area as a product.

	8
$3x^2$	

    c.   Kelly wants to find a shortcut to factor $2x^2 + 7x + 6$. She knows that $2x^2$ and 6 go into the rectangle in the locations shown at right. She also remembers Casey's pattern for diagonals. Without actually factoring yet, what do we know about the missing two parts of the generic rectangle?

	6
$2x^2$	

Continued on next page →

8*13.   *Continued from previous page*

product

sum

d.   To complete Kelly's generic rectangle, we need two x-terms that have a sum of $7x$ and a product of $12x^2$. Create and solve a Diamond Problem that represents this situation.

e.   Use your results from the Diamond Problem to complete the generic rectangle for $2x^2 + 7x + 6$ and then write the area as a product of factors.

8*14.   Factoring with a generic rectangle is especially convenient when algebra tiles are not available or when the number of necessary tiles becomes too large to manage. Using a Diamond Problem helps avoid guessing and checking, which can at times be challenging. Use the process from problem 8*13 to factor $6x^2 + 17x + 12$. The questions below will guide your process.

a.   When given a trinomial, such as $6x^2 + 17x + 12$, what two parts of a generic rectangle can you quickly complete?

b.   How can you set up a Diamond Problem to help factor a trinomial such as $6x^2 + 17x + 12$? What goes on top? What goes on bottom?

product

sum

c.   Solve the Diamond Problem for $6x^2 + 17x + 12$ and complete its generic rectangle. Then write the area of the rectangle as a product.

8*15.   Use the process you developed in problem 8*13 to factor the following quadratics, if possible. If a quadratic cannot be factored, **justify** your conclusion.

a. $x^2 + 9x + 18$
    b. $4x^2 + 17x - 15$

c. $4x^2 - 8x + 3$
    d. $3x^2 + 5x - 3$

METHODS AND MEANINGS

MATH NOTES

Diagonals of Generic Rectangles

Why does Casey's pattern from problem 8*4 work? That is, why does the product of the terms in one diagonal of a 2 by 2 generic rectangle always equal the product of the terms in the other diagonal?

Examine the generic rectangle at right for $(a + b)(c + d)$. Notice that each of the resulting diagonals have a product of $abcd$. Thus, the product of the terms in the diagonals are equal.

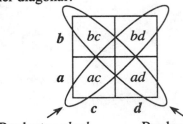
Product = $abcd$ Product = $abcd$

8*16.   Use the process you developed in problem 8*13 to factor the following quadratics, if possible.

    a. $x^2 - 4x - 12$ b. $4x^2 + 4x + 1$

    c. $2x^2 - 9x - 5$ d. $3x^2 + 10x - 8$

8*17.   For each rule represented below, state the x- and y-intercepts, if possible.

    a. 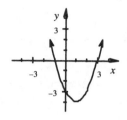   b.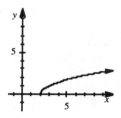

    c.

x	-5	-4	-3	-2	-1	0	1	2	3
y	8	4	0	-4	0	2	0	-4	-8

    d. $5x - 2y = 40$

8*18.   Graph $y = -x^2 + 9$ on graph paper.

    a.   Name the y-intercept. What is the **connection** between the y-intercept and the rule $y = -x^2 + 9$?

    b.   Name the x-intercepts. What is the **connection** between the x-intercepts and the rule $y = -x^2 + 9$?

8*19.   Find the point of intersection for each system.

    a. $\begin{array}{l} y = 2x - 3 \\ x + y = 15 \end{array}$ b. $\begin{array}{l} 3x = y - 2 \\ 6x = 4 - 2y \end{array}$

8*20.   Solve.

    a. $\frac{4x}{5} = \frac{x-2}{7}$ b. $-3(2b - 7) = -3b + 21 - 3b$ c. $6 - 2(c - 3) = 12$

8*21.   Find the equation of the line which passes through the points (-800, 200) and (-400, 300).

Algebra Connections: Chapter 8

8.1.3 How can we factor this?

Factoring with Special Cases

Practice your new method for factoring quadratic expressions without tiles as you consider special types of quadratic expressions.

8*22. Factor each quadratic below, if possible. Use a Diamond Problem and generic rectangle for each one.

a. $x^2 + 6x + 9$ b. $2x^2 + 5x + 3$

c. $x^2 + 5x - 7$ d. $3m^2 + m - 14$

8*23. SPECIAL CASES

Most quadratics are written in the form $ax^2 + bx + c$. But what if a term is missing? What if the terms are in a different order? Consider these questions while factoring the expressions below. Share your ideas with your teammates and be prepared to demonstrate your process for the class.

a. $9x^2 - 4$ b. $12x^2 - 16x$

c. $3 + 8k^2 - 10k$ d. $40 - 100m$

8*24. Now turn your attention to the quadratic below. Use a generic rectangle and Diamond Problem to factor this expression. Compare your answer with your teammates. Is there more than one possible answer?

$$4x^2 - 10x - 6$$

8*25.   The multiplication table below has factors along the top row and left column. Their product is where the row and column intersect. With your team, complete the table with all the factors and products.

Multiply	$x-2$		
$x+7$			
	$3x^2-5x-2$	$6x^2+5x+1$	
	x^2-5x+6		x^2-9

8*26.   As a Learning Reflection, explain how to factor a quadratic expression. Be sure to offer examples to demonstrate your understanding. Include an explanation of how to deal with special cases, such as when a term is missing or when the terms are not in standard order. Title this entry "Factoring Quadratics" and include today's date.

METHODS AND MEANINGS

Standard Form of a Quadratic

MATH NOTES

A quadratic expression in the form ax^2+bx+c is said to be in **standard form**. Notice that the terms are in order from greatest exponent to least.

Examples of quadratic expressions in standard form:

$$x^2-9 \quad \text{and} \quad 3m^2+m-1$$

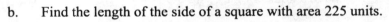

8*27. The perimeter of a triangle is 51 cm. The longest side is twice the length of the shortest side. The third side is 3 cm. longer than the shortest side. How long is each side? Write an equation that represents the problem and solve it.

8*28. Remember that a square is a rectangle with four equal sides.

   a. If a square has an area of 81 square units, how long is each side?

   b. Find the length of the side of a square with area 225 units.

   c. Find the length of the side of a square with area 10 units.

   d. Find the area of a square with side 11 units.

8*29. Factor the following quadratics, if possible.

   a. $k^2 - 12k + 20$ b. $6x^2 + 17x - 14$

   c. $x^2 - 8x + 16$ d. $9m^2 - 1$

8*30. Where do these two equations intersect? $y = 4x - 3$
                                                $y = 9x - 13$

8*31. Find the equation of a line perpendicular to the one graphed at right and passing through the point (6, 2).

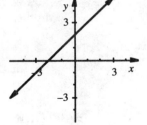

8*32. Solve each equation below for x. Check each solution.

   a. $2x - 10 = 0$ b. $x + 6 = 0$ c. $(2x - 10)(x + 6) = 0$

   d. $4x + 1 = 0$ e. $x - 8 = 0$ f. $(4x + 1)(x - 8) = 0$

8.1.4 Can we factor again?

Factoring Completely

There are many ways to write the number 12 as a product of factors. For example, 12 can be rewritten as $3 \cdot 4$, as $2 \cdot 6$, or as $2 \cdot 2 \cdot 3$. While each of these products is accurate, only $2 \cdot 2 \cdot 3$ is considered to be **factored completely**, since the factors are prime and cannot be factored themselves.

During this lesson we will consider what it means for a quadratic to be factored completely.

8*33.   Review what you have learned by factoring the following expressions, if possible.

     a. $9x^2 - 12x + 4$ b. $81m^2 - 1$

     c. $28 + x^2 - 11x$ d. $3n^2 + 9n + 6$

8*34.   Compare your solutions for problem 8*33 with the rest of your class.

     a.   Is there more than one factored form of $3n^2 + 9n + 6$? Why or why not?

     b.   Why does $3n^2 + 9n + 6$ have more than one factored form while the other quadratics in problem 8*33 only have one possible answer? Look for clues in the original expression ($3n^2 + 9n + 6$) and in the different factored forms.

     c.   **Without factoring**, predict which quadratic expressions below may have more than one factored form. Be prepared to defend your choice to the rest of the class.

         i. $12t^2 - 10t + 2$ ii. $5p^2 - 23p - 10$

         iii. $10x^2 + 25x - 15$ iv. $3k^2 + 7k - 6$

8*35.   FACTORING COMPLETELY

In part (c) of problem 8*34, you should have noticed that each term in $12t^2 - 10t + 2$ is divisible by 2. That is, it has a **common factor** of 2.

     a.   What is the common factor for $10x^2 + 25x - 15$?

Continued on next page →

8*35. *Continued from previous page*

b. In order to consider an expression **completely factored**, each factor must have all common factors separated out. Sometimes it is easiest to do this first. Since 5 is a common factor of $10x^2 + 25x - 15$, we can factor $10x^2 + 25x - 15$ using a special generic rectangle below. Find the length of this generic rectangle and write its area as a product of its length and width.

$$5 \begin{array}{|c|c|c|} \hline 10x^2 & +25x & -15 \\ \hline \end{array}$$

c. Can we factor further? That is, can either factor from the result from part (b) above also be factored? Factor any possible expressions and write your solution as a product of all three factors.

8*36. Factor each of the following expressions as completely as possible.

a. $5x^2 + 15x - 20$

b. $3x^3 - 6x^2 - 45x$

c. $2x^2 - 50$

d. $x^2y - 3xy - 10y$

METHODS AND MEANINGS

MATH NOTES

Factoring Quadratic Expressions

Review the process of factoring quadratics developed in problem 8*13 and outlined below. This example demonstrates how to factor $3x^2 + 10x + 8$.

1. Place the x^2 and constant terms of the quadratic expression in opposite corners of the generic rectangle. Determine the sum and product of the two remaining corners: The sum is simply the x-term of the quadratic expression, while the product is equal to the product of the x^2 and constant terms.

2. Place this sum and product into a Diamond Problem and solve.

3. Place the solutions from the Diamond Problem into the generic rectangle and find the dimensions of the generic rectangle.

4. Write your answer as a product: $(3x + 4)(x + 2)$.

8*37.   Factor the quadratic expressions below. If the quadratic is not factorable, explain why.

a. $2x^2 + 3x - 5$ b. $x^2 - x - 6$

c. $3x^2 + 13x + 4$ d. $2x^2 + 5x + 7$

8*38.   A line has intercepts (4, 0) and (0, -3). Find the equation of the line.

8*39.   As Jhalil and Joman practice for the SAT, their scores on practice tests rise. Jhalil's current score is 850, and it is rising by 10 points per week. On the other hand, Joman's current score is 570, and is growing by 50 points per week.

a.   When will Joman's score catch up to Jhalil's?

b.   If the SAT test is in 12 weeks, who will score highest?

8*40.   Mary says that you can find an x-intercept by substituting 0 for x, while Michelle says that you need to substitute 0 for y.

a.   Who, if anyone, is correct and why?

b.   Use the correct approach to find the x-intercept of $-4x + 5y = 16$.

8*41.   Find three consecutive numbers whose sum is 138. Write an equation and solve.

8*42.   Match each rule below with its corresponding graph. Can you do this without making any tables?

a. $y = -x^2 - 2$ b. $y = x^2 - 2$ c. $y = -x^2 + 2$

1.   2.   3.

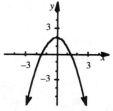   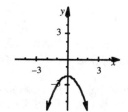   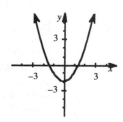

8.2.1 What do we know about a parabola?

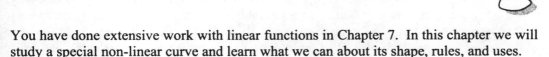

Investigating a Parabola

You have done extensive work with linear functions in Chapter 7. In this chapter we will study a special non-linear curve and learn what we can about its shape, rules, and uses.

8*43.　FUNCTIONS OF AMERICA

Congratulations! Your brochure for the Line Factory was so successful that the small local company grew into a national corporation called Functions of America. Recently, your company has had some growing pains and your new boss has turned to your team for help. See her memo below:

MEMO

To:　Your study team
From:　Ms. Freda Function, CEO
Re:　New product line

I have heard that while lines are very popular, there is a new craze in Europe to have non-linear designs. I recently visited Paris and Milan and discovered that we are behind the times!

Please investigate a new function called a parabola. I'd like a full report at the end of today with any information your team can give me about its shape and equation. Spare no detail! I'd like to know everything you can tell me about how the rule for a parabola affects its shape. I'd also like to know about any special points on a parabola or any patterns that exist in its table.

Remember, the company is only as good as its employees! I need you to uncover the secrets that our competitors do not know.

Sincerely, Ms. Function, CEO

Your Task: Your team will be assigned its own parabola to study. Investigate your team's parabola and be ready to describe everything you can about it by using its graph, rule, and table. Answer the questions below to get your investigation started. You may answer them in any order; however, do not limit yourselves to these questions!

- Does your parabola have any symmetry? That is, can you fold the graph of your parabola so that each side of the fold exactly matches the other? If so, where would the fold be? Do you think this works for all parabolas? Why or why not?

Continued on next page →

8*43.   *Continued from previous page*

- What is the highest point possible on your parabola? Is there one? What about the lowest point possible? What can you say about high and low points for all parabolas? The **vertex** is the name of the highest or lowest point on the parabola. It is the point where the parabola turns.

- Are there any special points on your parabola? Which points do you think are important to know? Are there any special points that you expected but do not exist for your parabola? What **connection**(s) do these points have with the rule of your parabola?

- How would you describe the shape of your parabola? For example, would you describe your parabola as pointing upward or downward? Do the sides of the parabola ever go straight up or down (vertically)? Why or why not? Is there anything else special about its shape?

Parabola list:

$$y = x^2 - 2x - 8$$ $$y = -x^2 + 4$$

$$y = x^2 - 4x + 5$$ $$y = -x^2 - 2x - 1$$

$$y = x^2 - 6x + 5$$ $$y = -x^2 + 3x + 4$$

8*44.   Prepare a poster for the CEO detailing your findings from your parabola investigation. Include any insights you and your teammates found. Explain your conclusions and **justify** your statements. Remember to include a complete graph of your parabola with all special points carefully labeled.

![L]OOKING DEEPER

MATH NOTES

Symmetry

When a graph or picture can be folded so that both sides will perfectly match, it is said to have **symmetry**. The line where the fold would be is called the **line of symmetry**. Some shapes have more than one line of symmetry. See the examples below.

This shape has
one line of
symmetry

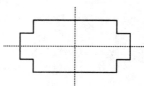

This shape has
two lines of
symmetry

This shape has
eight lines of
symmetry

This graph has
two lines of
symmetry

Algebra Connections: Chapter 8

8*45. Calculate the expressions below.

a. $\dfrac{2+\sqrt{16}}{3}$

b. $\dfrac{-1+\sqrt{49}}{-2}$

c. $\dfrac{-10-\sqrt{5}}{2}$

8*46. Find the equation of the line through the points (-15, 70) and (5, 10).

8*47. For each rule represented below, state the x- and y-intercepts.

a.
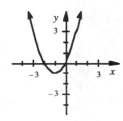

b.
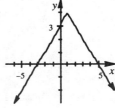

c.

x	-3	-2	-1	0	1	2	3
y	8	3	0	-1	0	3	8

d. $2x + 3y = 18$

8*48. Change $6x - 2y = 10$ to $y = mx + b$ form. Then state the slope (m) and the y-intercept (b).

8*49. Copy the figure at right onto your paper. Then draw any lines of symmetry.

8*50. Use a generic rectangle to multiply $(3x - 4)(2x + 3)$.

8.2.2 What are the connections for quadratics?

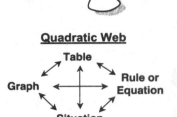

Quadratic Representations

In Chapter 4 you completed a web for the different representations of linear equations. You discovered special shortcuts to help you move from one representation to another. For example, given a linear equation you can now draw the corresponding graph as well as determine an equation from a graph.

Quadratic Web

Today you will explore the **connections** between the different representations for quadratics. As you work, keep in mind the following questions:

What representations am I using?

What is the connection between the various representations?

What do I know about a parabola?

8*51.   Many objects and motions have parabolas hidden in them. For instance, the motion of a rollercoaster going over a hill might look like a downward-facing parabola. Several partial parabolas are shown below. For each parabola or part of a parabola, find a situation or object that it could represent.

a.   b.   c.   d.

8*52.   WATER BALLOON CONTEST

Every year Newtown High School holds a water balloon competition during halftime of their Homecoming game. Each contestant uses a catapult to launch a water balloon from the ground on the football field. This year you are the judge! You must decide which contestants win the prizes for *Longest Distance* and *Highest Launch*.
Fortunately, you have a computer that will collect data for each throw. The computer uses x to represent horizontal distance in yards from the goal line and y to represent the height in yards.

Continued on next page →

8*52. *Continued from previous page*

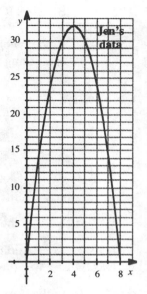

The announcer shouts, "Maggie Nanimos, you're up first!" She runs down and places her catapult at the 3-yard line. After Maggie's launch, the computer reports that the balloon traveled along the parabola $y = -x^2 + 17x - 42$.

Then you hear, "Jen Erus, you're next!" Jen runs down to the field, places her catapult at the goal line, and releases the balloon. The tracking computer reports the path of the balloon with the graph at right.

The third contestant, Imp Ecable, accidentally launches the balloon before you are ready. The balloon launches, you hear a roar from the crowd, turn around, and...SPLAT! The balloon soaks you and your computer! You only have time to write down the following partial information about the balloon's path before your computer fizzles:

x (yards)	2	3	4	5	6	7	8	9
y (yards)	0	9	16	21	24	25	24	21

Finally, the announcer calls for the last contestant, Albert Truistic. With your computer broken, you decide to record the balloon's height and distance by hand. Albert releases the balloon from the 10-yard line. The ball reaches a height of 27 yards, and lands at the 16-yard line.

a. Obtain the Lesson 8.2.2 Resource Page from your teacher. For each contestant, create a table and graph using the information provided by the computer. Determine which of these contestants should win the *Longest Distance* and *Highest Throw* contests.

b. Find the *x*-intercepts of each parabola (also called **roots**). What information do the *x*-intercepts tell you about each balloon toss?

c. Find the vertex of each parabola. What information does the vertex tell you about each balloon throw?

8*53. Today you have explored the four different representations of quadratics: table, graph, equation, and a description of a physical situation involving motion. Draw the web at right on your paper and label it "Quadratic Web."

Quadratic Web

Table

Graph   **Rule or Equation**

Situation

a. Draw in arrows showing the **connections** that you currently know how to make between different representations. Be prepared to **justify** a connection for the class.

b. What connections are still missing?

8*54.   SITUATION TO RULE

Review how to write a rule from a situation by
examining the tile pattern below.

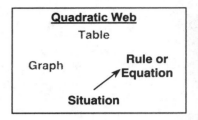

Quadratic Web

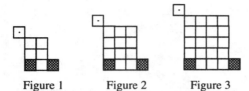

Figure 1   Figure 2   Figure 3

a.   Write a rule to represent the number of tiles in Figure x.

b.   Is the rule from part (a) **quadratic**? Explain how you know.

c.   Add this pathway to your web from problem 8*53.

8*55.   In the next few days you will work on adding additional pathways
and shortcuts to help you move between representations. Copy your
"Quadratic Web" from problem 8*53 as a Learning Reflection so that
you can refer back to it later.

8*56.   Graph $y = x^2 - 8x + 7$ and label its vertex, x-, and y-intercepts.

8*57.   What is special about the number zero? Think about this as you answer the questions
below.

a.   Find each sum:

$0 + 3 =$ $-7 + 0 =$ $0 + 6 =$ $0 + (-2) =$

b.   What is special about adding zero? Write a sentence
that begins, "When you add zero to a number, …"

c.   Julia is thinking of two numbers a and b. When she
adds them together, she gets a sum of b. Does that tell
you anything about either of Julia's numbers?

d.   Find each product:

$3 \cdot 0 =$ $(-7) \cdot 0 =$ $0 \cdot 6 =$

e.   What is special about multiplying by zero? Write a sentence that begins, "When
you multiply a number by zero, …"

8*58. For each rule represented below, state the *x*- and *y*-intercepts.

a.

x	y
2	0
0	18
-4	0
-1	-8
6	22
3	0

b.

x	y
7	-4
3	0
10	8
0	-3
8	0
-7	-1

c.

x	y
0	-4
-5	11
3	-2
1	0
13	27
-6	14

8*59. For the line $y = 2x + 6$:

a. What is the *x*-intercept?

b. What is the slope of any line perpendicular to the given line?

8*60. Solve the following systems of equations using any method. Check your solution if possible.

a. $6x - 2y = 10$
$3x - y = 2$

b. $x - 3y = 1$
$y = 16 - 2x$

8.2.3 How are quadratic rules and graphs connected?

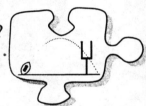

Zero Product Property

You already know a lot about quadratics and parabolas and you have made several **connections** between their different representations on the Quadratic Web. Today you are going to develop a method to sketch a parabola from its equation without a table.

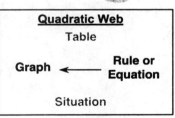

Quadratic Web

Table

Graph ⟵ Rule or Equation

Situation

8*61. WHAT DO YOU NEED TO SKETCH A PARABOLA?

How many points do you need in order to sketch a parabola? 1? 10? 50? Think about this as you answer the questions below. Note: a sketch does not need to be exact. The parabola merely needs to be reasonably placed with important points clearly labeled.

a. Can you sketch a parabola if you only know where its *y*-intercept is? For example, if the *y*-intercept of a parabola is at (0, -15), can you sketch its graph? Why or why not?

Continued on next page →

8*61.   *Continued from previous page*

b.   What about the two x-intercepts (also called **roots**) of the parabola? If you only know where the x-intercepts are, can you draw the parabola? For example, if the roots (x-intercepts) are at (-3, 0) and (5, 0), can you predict the path of the parabola?

c.   Can you sketch a parabola with only its roots (x-intercepts) and y-intercept? To test this idea, sketch the graph of a parabola $y = x^2 - 2x - 15$ with the roots (-3, 0) and (5, 0) and the y-intercept at (0, -15).

8*62.   Problem 8*61 established that if we can find the intercepts of a parabola from a rule, then we can sketch its graph without a table.

a.   As mentioned in problem 8*61, another name for an x-intercept is a **root**. Therefore, the **roots** of a parabola are simply its x-intercepts.

What is true about the value of y for all roots (x-intercepts)? What is true about the value of x for all y-intercepts? Review your knowledge of intercepts and describe it here.

b.   If $x = 0$ at the y-intercept, find the y-intercept of $y = 2x^2 + 5x - 12$.

c.   If a root (x-intercept) occurs when $y = 0$, write an equation that would help find the roots (x-intercepts) of $y = 2x^2 + 5x - 12$.

d.   At this point, can you solve your equation in part (c) for x? Explain why or why not.

8*63.   ZERO PRODUCT PROPERTY

The equation you wrote in part (c) of problem 8*62 is called a **Quadratic Equation**. To solve it, we need to examine what we know about zero. Use the game below to study zero's special properties.

Nathan, Nancy, and Gaston are playing a game where Nathan and Nancy each think of a number and then give Gaston a clue about their numbers.
Using the clue, Gaston must tell them everything that he knows about their numbers.

a.   Nathan and Nancy's first clue for Gaston is that when you multiply their numbers together, the result is zero. What conclusion can Gaston make?

b.   Disappointed that Gaston came so close to figuring out their numbers, Nathan and Nancy invite Nadia over to make things harder. Nathan, Nancy, and Nadia all think of secret numbers. This time Gaston is told that when their *three* secret numbers are multiplied together, the answer is zero. What can Gaston conclude this time?

Continued on next page →

8*63.   *Continued from previous page*

    c.   Does it matter how many numbers are multiplied? If the product is zero, what do you know about one of the numbers? This property is called the **Zero Product Property**. With your class, write a description of this property. Title this entry "Zero Product Property" and include today's date in your Learning Reflection.

8*64.   How can we use the Zero Product Property to help us solve our quadratic equation $0 = 2x^2 + 5x - 12$ from part (c) of problem 8*62?

    a.   Examine the quadratic equation. Is there a product that equals zero? If not, how can you rewrite the quadratic expression as a product?

    b.   Now that the equation is written as a product of factors equaling zero, we can use the Zero Product Property to solve it. Since we know that one of the factors must be zero, we can set up two smaller equations to help us solve for x. Use one factor at a time and determine what x-value makes it equal to zero.

    c.   What do these solutions represent? What do they tell us?

    d.   You now know all the intercepts for the parabola $y = 2x^2 + 5x - 12$. Use the special points to sketch a graph of the parabola.

8*65.   Use a similar process to sketch the parabola $y = x^2 + x - 6$ by using its intercepts.

8*66.   Sketch the parabola $y = 2x^2 + 6x + 4$ by using its intercepts.

METHODS AND MEANINGS

Zero Product Property

When the product of two or more numbers is zero, one of those numbers must be zero. This is known as the **Zero Product Property**. If the two numbers are a and b, this property can be written as follows:

If a and b are two numbers where $a \cdot b = 0$, then $a = 0$ or $b = 0$.

For example, if $(2x - 3)(x + 5) = 0$, then $2x - 3 = 0$ or $x + 5 = 0$. Solving yields the solutions $x = \frac{3}{2}$ or $x = -5$. This property helps us solve quadratic equations when the equation can be written as a product of factors.

8*67.   Compare the two equations below.

$$(x+2)(x-1) = 0 \text{ and } (x+2)+(x-1) = 0$$

   a.   How are these equations different?

   b.   Solve both equations.

8*68.   Solve for x.

   a. $(x-2)(x+8) = 0$ b. $(3x-9)(x-1) = 0$

   c. $(x+10)(2x-5) = 0$ d. $(3x+4)(2x-12) = 0$

8*69.   Examine the system of equations below.

$$5x - 2y = 4$$
$$x = 0$$

   a.   Before solving this system, Danielle noticed that the point of intersection is also the x-intercept of $5x - 2y = 4$. Explain how she knows this.

   b.   Find the point of intersection of the two rules above.

8*70.   The roots (x-intercepts) of $y = 2x^2 - 16x + 30$ are (3, 0) and (5, 0).

   a.   What is the x-coordinate of the vertex?

   b.   Use your answer to part (a) above to find the y-coordinate of the vertex. Then write the vertex as a point (x, y).

8*71.   Factor each quadratic below completely.

   a. $2x^2 - 2x - 4$ b. $6x^2 - 27x - 15$

8*72.   The symbol "≤" represents "less than or equal to" while the symbol "<" represents "less than."

   a.   Similarly translate "≥" and ">."

   b.   How can you write an expression that states that 5 is greater than 3?

   c.   Write another expression that states that x is less than or equal to 9.

   d.   Translate the expression $-2 < 7$ into words.

8.2.4 What new connection can we make?

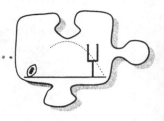

Solving Quadratic Equations by Factoring

In Lesson 8.2.3, you developed a method for finding the roots (*x*-intercepts) of a parabola without a table. Today you will learn how to use that skill to solve a wide array of quadratic equations.

You will also revisit the quadratic web, make a **connection** between the table and rule of a parabola, and then **apply** this connection to the water balloon competition.

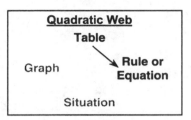

8*73.   Review what you learned in Lesson 8.2.3 by sketching the graph of $y = x^2 + 3x + 2$ without a table. Specifically, find the roots (*x*-intercepts) and the *y*-intercept of the parabola and sketch its graph.

8*74.   Part of finding the roots (*x*-intercepts) of a parabola involves creating and solving a quadratic equation of the form $ax^2 + bx + c = 0$. Practice using the Zero Product Property by solving the quadratic equations below.

   a. $x^2 + 6x + 8 = 0$ b. $0 = 3x^2 - 7x + 4$

   c. $(x + 5)(-2x + 3) = 0$ d. $x^2 + 6x = 0$

   e. $0 = 3(x - 5)(2x + 3)$

8*75.   TABLE TO RULE

   You know how to make a table for a quadratic rule, but how can we write an equation when given the table? Examine this new **connection** that requires you to **reverse** your understanding of the Zero Product Property as you find a rule for each table below. What clues in the tables helped you find the rule?

   a.
x	-4	-3	-2	-1	0	1	2	3	4
y	6	0	-4	-6	-6	-4	0	6	14

   b.
x	-6	-5	-4	-3	-2	-1	0	1	2	3	4
y	7	0	-5	-8	-9	-8	-5	0	7	16	27

8*76.   WATER BALLOON CONTEST REVISITED

Remember Imp's water balloon toss? Since the
water balloon was thrown on the computer, you
were given only a table of data, shown again
below. Find a rule that represents the height of Imp's
balloon as it traveled through the air.

x (yards)	2	3	4	5	6	7	8	9
y (yards)	0	9	16	21	24	25	24	21

8*77.   Find the quadratic web in your Learning Reflection from Lesson
8.2.3. In this journal entry, add a short explanation for how to find a
quadratic equation from its table. Then add an arrow to your web, for
the **connection** you made today.

8*78.   What is the result when $65x^2 + 212x - 133$ is factored and then the factors are
multiplied together? How did you find your answer?

8*79.   Solve the equations below for x. Check your solutions.

a. $(6x - 18)(3x + 2) = 0$ b. $x^2 - 7x + 10 = 0$

c. $2x^2 + 2x - 12 = 0$ d. $4x^2 - 1 = 0$

8*80.   Sketch each parabola below with the given information.

a.   A parabola with roots (x-intercepts) (2, 0) and (7, 0), and
with y-intercept (0, -8).

b.   A parabola with exactly one root at (-1, 0) and with the y-
intercept at (0, 3).

c.   The parabola $y = (x + 5)(x - 1)$.

8*81. Review the meanings of the inequality symbols in the box at right. Then decide if the statements below are true or false.

a. $5 < 7$ b. $-2 \geq 9$ c. $0 \leq 0$

d. $-5 > -10$ e. $16 \leq -16$ f. $1 > 1$

$<$	less than
$\leq$	less than or equal to
$>$	more than
$\geq$	more than or equal to

8*82. Calculate the expressions below with a scientific calculator.

a. $\dfrac{-10 + \sqrt{25}}{5}$ b. $\dfrac{8 + \sqrt{40}}{3 \cdot 3}$ c. $\dfrac{8 + \sqrt{3^2 + 2 \cdot 3 + 1}}{-4}$

8*83. Find the equation of the line through the points (6, -8) and (0, 0).

a. What is the slope of the line?

b. Is the point (3, -4) on the line? How can you tell?

8.2.5 What can we do with quadratics now?

Completing the Quadratic Web

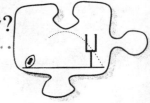

In just three lessons you have almost completed the quadratic representation web. Revisit the web posted in your classroom. What **connection**(s) still need to be made?

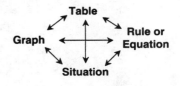

Today you will focus on how to get a quadratic rule from a graph and a situation. As you work, ask the following questions:

Which representation am I given? Which am I looking for?

How can I **reverse** this process?

Is there another way?

8*84. Several parabolas and quadratic rules are shown below. Match each parabola with its rule. **Justify** your choices and share any shortcuts you find with your teammates. (**Note**: Not every rule will be matched with a parabola.)

(1)
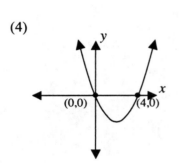

(2)
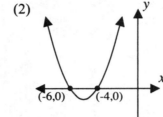

(3)
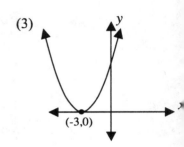

(4)

(5)
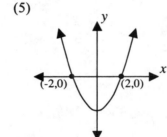

(6)
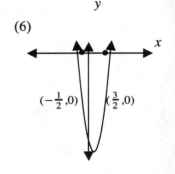

a. $y = (x+3)^2$

b. $y = x^2 + 3x - 28$

c. $y = x^2 - 11x + 28$

d. $y = x^2 - 4$

e. $y = x^2 + 10x + 24$

f. $y = 2x^2 + 11x + 5$

g. $y = x^2 - 4x$

h. $y = (x-3)^2$

i. $y = 4x^2 - 4x - 3$

8*85.   QUALITY CONTROL: Part 1

Congratulations! With your promotion you are now the Quality Assurance Representative of the Function Factory. Your job is to make sure your clients are happy. Whenever a client writes to the company, you must reply with clear directions that will solve his or her problem.

Your boss has provided graphing technology and a team of fellow employees to help you fulfill your job description.

Your Task:

1.   Carefully read the complaints below. Study each situation with your grapher. Work with your team to resolve each situation.

2.   Write each customer a friendly response that offers a solution to his or her problem. Remember that the customers are not parabola experts! Do not assume that they know anything about parabolas.

A

Dear Ms. Quadratic,

I followed all the directions given in your brochure on how to order a parabola. I specifically ordered a parabola only to have you send me the wrong one! I want the parabola to pass through the points (1, 0) and (-6, 0).

Please tell me how to order the correct parabola. Your immediate reply is appreciated.

Perturbed in Pennsylvania

B

Dear Miss Quadratic,

I am a very dissatisfied customer. I want a parabola that hits the x-axis only <u>once</u> at (5, 0), yet I see NO mention of this type of parabola in your pamphlet. Your company mission statement assures me that "my needs will be met no matter what." How should I order my special parabola?

Sincerely,

Troubled in Texas

C

Dear Ms. Quadratic,

Please help! I have searched through your entire brochure and did not see a parabola that would fit my needs. All I want is a parabola that looks like this:

Every time I order an equation to give me this parabola you always send me a different one! I refuse to pay for any parabola but the one shown above. Please tell me how I should find the equation of this parabola or I will take my business elsewhere!

Thank you,

Agitated in Alaska

Quadratics

8*86.   **EXTRA! EXTRA!**

A journalist from the school newspaper wants to publish the results from the water balloon contest. She wants a rule for each toss, so that she can program her computer to create a graph for her article. You already have rules for the tosses made by Maggie and Imp from problems 8*52 and 8*76.

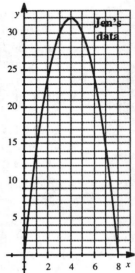

a.   Examine the graph at right that represents the height of Jen's toss. Find the rule for this parabola.

b.   Albert released his balloon from the 10-yard line and it landed at the 16-yard line. If the ball reached a height of 27 yards, what equation represents the path of his toss?

8*87.   **QUALITY CONTROL: Part 2**

Lots O'Dough, a wealthy customer, would like to order a variety of parabolas. However, he is feeling pressed for time and said that he will pay you *lots* of extra money if you complete his order for him. Of course you agreed! He sent you sketches of each parabola that he would like to receive. Determine a possible equation for each parabola so that you may pass this information on to the Manufacturing Department.

a.

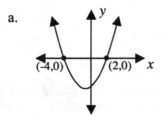

b.

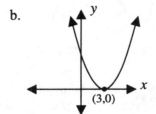

c.

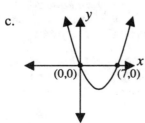

d.

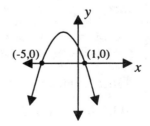

8*88.   Find the slope and y-intercept of the line $6y - 3x = 24$.

8*89.   Examine the graph of $y = 2x^2 + 2x - 1$ at right.

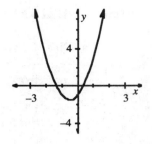

   a.   Estimate the roots (x-intercepts).

   b.   What happens if you try to use the Zero Product Property
          to find the x-intercepts?

8*90.   Solve the equations below for x. Check your solutions.

   a. $x^2 + 6x - 40 = 0$ b. $2x^2 + 13x - 24 = 0$

8*91.   Calculate the expressions below. Then compare your answers from (a) and (b) to those
          in problem 8*90. What do you notice?

   a. $\dfrac{-6 + \sqrt{6^2 - (4)(1)(-40)}}{2 \cdot 1}$ b. $\dfrac{-6 - \sqrt{6^2 - (4)(1)(-40)}}{2 \cdot 1}$

   c. $\dfrac{-13 - \sqrt{13^2 - (4)(2)(-24)}}{2 \cdot 2}$ d. $\dfrac{-13 + \sqrt{13^2 - (4)(2)(-24)}}{2 \cdot 2}$

8*92.   Use any method to solve the systems of equations below.

   a. $2x - 3y = 5$ b. $m = -3 + 2n$
          $4x + y = 3$ $4m + 6n = -5$

8.3.1 What if we can't factor?

Introduction to the Quadratic Formula

In Section 8.2 you developed a method to find the roots (x-intercepts) of a parabola by factoring
and using the Zero Product Property. Today you will learn a new method to solve quadratic
equations.

8*93.   Use the Zero Product Property to find the roots of $y = x^2 - 3x - 7$.

   a.   What happened?

   b.   What does this result tell you about the roots?

   c.   Your teacher will display the graph of this parabola for the class. Did the graph
          confirm your answer to part (b)? Estimate the roots using the graph.

8*94. **QUADRATIC FORMULA**

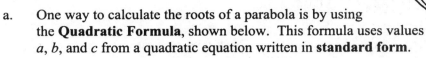

Since a parabola can have roots even when its quadratic equation is not factorable, we need another way to find the roots from a rule.

a. One way to calculate the roots of a parabola is by using the **Quadratic Formula**, shown below. This formula uses values a, b, and c from a quadratic equation written in **standard form**.

$$x = \frac{-b \pm \sqrt{b^2 - 4ac}}{2a}$$

When the quadratic equation is written in **standard form** (i.e., it looks like $ax^2 + bx + c = 0$), then a is the number of x^2 terms, b is the number of x terms, and c is the constant. If $x^2 - 3x - 7 = 0$, then what are a, b, and c?

b. The Quadratic Formula calculates **two** possible answers by using the "±" symbol. This symbol (read as "plus or minus") is shorthand notation that tells us to calculate the formula twice: once with addition and once with subtraction in the numerator. Therefore, every Quadratic Formula problem is really two different problems:

$$x = \frac{-b + \sqrt{b^2 - 4ac}}{2a} \quad \text{and} \quad x = \frac{-b - \sqrt{b^2 - 4ac}}{2a}$$

Carefully substitute a, b, and c for $x^2 - 3x - 7 = 0$ into the quadratic formula. Evaluate each expression (once using addition and once using subtraction) to solve for x. Do these solutions match those from part (c) of problem 8*93?

8*95. The Quadratic Formula is only one of the tools you can use to solve quadratic equations like $x^2 - 3x - 7 = 0$.

a. What are the other methods that you can use?

b. You may be thinking, "Where did this formula come from? Why does it work?" We can find the formula by starting with a generic quadratic $ax^2 + bx + c = 0$ and using our algebra skills to solve for x. See the Math Notes box for this lesson that details one way this formula can be derived. Later, in Chapter 12, you will learn another formal method to derive the Quadratic Formula.

8*96. Use the Quadratic Formula to solve the equations below for x, if possible. Check your solutions.

a. $3x^2 + 7x + 2 = 0$ b. $2x^2 - 9x - 35 = 0$

c. $8x^2 + 10x + 3 = 0$ d. $x^2 - 5x + 9 = 0$

8*97. As a Learning Reflection, describe how to use the Quadratic Formula. Be sure to include an example. Title this entry "Quadratic Formula" and include today's date.

       Algebra Connections: Chapter 8

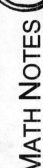
LOOKING DEEPER

Deriving the Quadratic Formula

Why is $x = \frac{-b \pm \sqrt{b^2 - 4ac}}{2a}$ a solution of $ax^2 + bx + c = 0$? One way to derive this formula is shown below.

1. Begin with the quadratic equation in standard form.

   $$ax^2 + bx + c = 0$$

2. Multiply each side by $4a$ and add b^2 to each side.

   $$4a(ax^2 + bx + c) + b^2 = b^2$$

3. Subtract $4ac$ from each side in order to get a factorable quadratic on the left.

   $$4a^2x^2 + 4abx + b^2 = b^2 - 4ac$$

4. The left side can be factored as $(2ax + b)^2$, which is demonstrated in the generic rectangle shown at right.

b	$2abx$	b^2
$2ax$	$4a^2x^2$	$2abx$
	$2ax$	b

5. Take the square root of each side to eliminate the exponent on the left side. Since both the positive and negative values of a number can be squared to give the same result (for example: 4^2 and $(-4)^2$ both equal 16), then we have two possible square root values: $(b^2 - 4ac)$ and $-(b^2 - 4ac)$.

   $$2ax + b = \pm\sqrt{b^2 - 4ac}$$

6. Now continue to solve for x by subtracting b from both sides and dividing by $2a$. Notice that a cannot equal zero or else we will get an error! However, if $a = 0$, then this equation would not be quadratic and we would not use this formula.

   $$2ax = -b \pm \sqrt{b^2 - 4ac}$$

7. Thus, $\frac{-b \pm \sqrt{b^2 - 4ac}}{2a}$ are solutions to the quadratic equation $ax^2 + bx + c = 0$.

   $$x = \frac{-b \pm \sqrt{b^2 - 4ac}}{2a}$$

8*98.   Solve the following quadratic equations by factoring and using the Zero Product Property. Be sure to check your solutions.

   a. $x^2 - 13x + 42 = 0$ b. $0 = 3x^2 + 10x - 8$

   c. $2x^2 - 10x = 0$ d. $4x^2 + 8x - 60 = 0$

8*99.   Use the Quadratic Formula to solve $x^2 - 13x + 42 = 0$. Did your solution match the solution from part (a) of problem 8*98?

8*100.   Does a quadratic equation always have two solutions? That is, does a parabola always intersect the x-axis twice?

   a.   If possible, draw an example of a parabola that only intersects the x-axis once.

   b.   What does it mean if the quadratic equation has no solution? Draw a possible parabola that would cause this to happen.

8*101.   Find the equation of the line through the point (-2, 8) with slope $\frac{1}{2}$.

8*102.   For each of the following equations indicate whether its graph would be a line or a parabola.

   a. $5x + 2y = 7$ b. $y = 3x^2$

   c. $y = 3$ d. $4x^2 + 3x = 7 + y$

8*103.   **Multiple Choice:** Which equations below are equivalent to:

$$\tfrac{1}{2}(6x - 14) + 5x = 2 - 3x + 8?$$

   a. $3x - 7 + 5x = 10 - 3x$ b. $3x - 14 + 5x = 2 - 3x + 8$

   c. $8x - 14 = 10 - 3x$ d. $6x - 14 + 10x = 4 - 6x + 16$

8*104.   Review the descriptions for the inequality symbols $<, \leq, >$, and $\geq$ in problem 8*81. Then decide if the statements below are true or false.

   a. $11 < -13$ b. $5 \cdot 2 \geq 10$ c. $13 > -3(2 - 6)$ d. $\left|-5\right| > 2$

   e. $9 \geq -9$ f. $-2 > -2$ g. $-16 < -15$ h. $0 > 6$

Algebra Connections: Chapter 8

8.3.2 How can I solve this quadratic equation?

More Solving Quadratic Equations

Today, you will **apply** and extend what you know about solving quadratic equations.

8*105. For the quadratic equation $6x^2 + 11x - 10 = 0$,

    a. Solve it using the Zero Product Property.

    b. Solve it using the Quadratic Formula.

    c. Did the solutions from parts (a) and (b) match? If not, why not?

8*106. As the Math Notes box from Lesson 8.3.1 demonstrated, the Quadratic Formula can solve any quadratic equation $ax^2 + bx + c = 0$ if $a \neq 0$. But what if the equation is not in standard form? What if terms are missing? Consider these questions as you solve the quadratic equations below. Share your ideas with your teammates and be prepared to demonstrate your process for the class.

    a. $4x^2 - 121 = 0$ b. $2x^2 - 2 - 3x = 0$

    c. $15x^2 - 165x = 630$ d. $36x^2 + 25 = 60x$

8*107. THE SAINT LOUIS GATEWAY ARCH

The Saint Louis Gateway Arch (pictured at right) has a shape much like a parabola. Suppose the Gateway Arch can be approximated by $y = 630 - 0.00635x^2$, where both x and y represent distances in feet and the origin is the point on the ground directly below the arch's apex (its highest point).

    a. Find the x-intercepts of the Gateway Arch. What does this information tell you? Use a calculator to evaluate your answers.

    b. How wide is the arch at its base?

    c. How tall is the arch? How did you find your solution?

    d. Draw a quick sketch of the arch on graph paper, labeling the axes with all the values you know.

Ⓛ OOKING DEEPER

Simplifying Square Roots and the Real Numbers

Before calculators were universally available, people who wanted to use approximate decimal values for numbers like $\sqrt{45}$ had other techniques available to them:

1. Carry around copies of long square root tables.

2. Use Guess and Check repeatedly to get desired accuracy.

3. "Simplify" the square roots. A square root is **simplified** when there are no more perfect square factors (square numbers such as 4, 25, and 81) under the radical sign.

Simplifying square roots was by far the fastest method. People factored the number as the product of integers hoping to find at least one perfect square number. They memorized approximations of the square roots of the integers from one to ten. Then they could figure out the decimal value by multiplying these memorized facts with the roots of the square numbers. Here is an example of this method.

Example: Simplify $\sqrt{45}$.

Rewrite $\sqrt{45}$ in an equivalent factored form.

Factor 45 so that one of the factors is a perfect square.

Simplify the square root of the perfect square.

$$\sqrt{45} = \sqrt{9 \cdot 5}$$
$$= \sqrt{9} \cdot \sqrt{5}$$
$$= 3\sqrt{5}$$

Verify with your calculator that both $3\sqrt{5}$ and $\sqrt{45} \approx 6.71$. Here are two more examples:

$$\sqrt{27}$$
$$= \sqrt{9}\sqrt{3}$$
$$= 3\sqrt{3}$$

$$\sqrt{72}$$
$$= \sqrt{36}\sqrt{2}$$
$$= 6\sqrt{2}$$

Note: We chose to write $\sqrt{72}$ as $\sqrt{36} \cdot \sqrt{2}$, rather than $\sqrt{9} \cdot \sqrt{8}$ or $\sqrt{4} \cdot \sqrt{18}$, because 36 is the largest perfect square factor of 72. However, since

$$\sqrt{4} \cdot \sqrt{18} = 2\sqrt{9 \cdot 2} = 2\sqrt{9} \cdot \sqrt{2} = 2 \cdot 3\sqrt{2} = 6\sqrt{2}$$

we can still get the same answer if we do it using different methods.

Continued on next page →

Continued from previous page

When you take the square root of an integer that is not a perfect square, the result is a decimal that never terminates or repeats. This result is called an **irrational number**. The irrational numbers and the rational numbers together form the numbers we use in this course, which are called **real numbers.**

Generally, since we live in the age of technology, when we want a decimal approximation of an irrational square root we use a calculator. But for an exact answer we must write the number using the $\sqrt{}$ symbol.

Review & Preview

8*108. Solve the following quadratic equations by factoring and using the Zero Product Property. Then check your solution.

a. $x^2 - 10x + 25 = 0$ b. $y = 3x^2 + 17x - 6$

c. $3x^2 - 2x = 5$ d. $16x^2 - 9 = 0$

8*109. Use the Quadratic Formula to solve part (b) of problem 8*108 above. Did your solution match the solution you got by factoring and using the Zero Product Property (in part (b) of problem 8*108)?

8*110. Find a possible equation for each parabola below based on the given information.

a.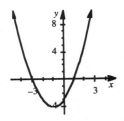

b.

x	-4	-3	-2	-1	0	1	2	3	4
y	12	5	0	-3	-4	-3	0	5	12

8*111. Solve the following problem using Guess and Check. Write an equation and then write your solution as a sentence.

The length of a rectangle is 5 cm longer than twice the length of the width. If the area of the rectangle is 403 square centimeters, how long is the width?

8*112. Which of the points below make the equation $4x - 3y = 10$ true? Note: more than one point may make this equation true.

a. (1, 2)   b. (4, 2)   c. (7, 6)   d. (4, -3)

8*113.   Kristen loves shortcuts. She figured out that she can find x- and y-intercepts for any line without graphing! For example, she knows that the x-intercept for $5x - 3y = 15$ is $(3, 0)$ just by examining the rule.

   a.   What is her shortcut?

   b.   Does this shortcut work for the y-intercept? Try it and then test your result by changing $5x - 3y = 15$ into $y = mx + b$ form.

   c.   Use this shortcut to find the x- and y-intercept of $3x - 2y = 24$.

8.3.3 Which method is best?

Choosing a Strategy

8*114.   You now have two algebraic methods to solve quadratic equations: using the Zero Product Property and using the Quadratic Formula. How can you decide which strategy is best to try first? Examine the quadratic equations below with your team. For each equation:

   •   Decide which strategy is best to try first.

   •   Solve the equation. If your first strategy does not work, switch to the other strategy.

   •   Check your solution(s).

   Be prepared to share your process with the class.

   a. $x^2 + 12x + 27 = 0$ b. $0.5x^2 + 9x + 3.2 = 0$

   c. $(3x + 4)(2x - 1) = 0$ d. $x^2 + 16 = 8x$

   e. $x^2 + 5 - 2x = 0$ f. $20x^2 - 30x = 2x + 45$

8*115.   With your class, decide when it is best to solve a quadratic by factoring and when you should go directly to the Quadratic Formula. Copy your observations as a Learning Reflection. Title this entry "Choosing a Strategy to Solve Quadratics" and include today's date.

8*116. While solving $(x-5)(x+2) = -6$, Kyle decided that x must equal 5 or –2. "Not so fast!" exclaimed Stanton, "The product does not equal zero. We need to change the equation first."

    a.   What is Stanton talking about?

    b.   How can the equation be rewritten? Discuss this with your team and use your algebraic tools to rewrite the equation so that it can be solved.

    c.   Solve your equation for x. Do your solutions match Kyle's?

8*117. MOE'S YO

Moe is playing with a yo-yo. He throws the yo-yo down and then pulls it back up. The motion of the yo-yo is represented by the equation $y = 2x^2 - 4.8x$, where x represents the number of seconds since the yo-yo left Moe's hand, and y represents the vertical height of the yo-yo with respect to Moe's hand. Note that when the yo-yo is in Moe's hand, $y = 0$, and when the yo-yo is below his hand, y is negative.

    a.   How long is Moe's yo-yo in the air before it comes back to Moe's hand? How did you find your answer? Use the Quadratic Formula to find the times that the yo-yo is in Moe's hand.

    b.   At what time does the yo-yo turn around? Use what you know about parabolas to help you.

    c.   How long is the yo-yo's string? That is, what is y when the yo-yo changes direction?

    d.   Draw a sketch of the graph representing the motion of Moe's yo-yo. On the sketch, label the important points: when the yo-yo is in Moe's hand and when it changes direction.

MATH NOTES METHODS AND MEANINGS

Solving a Quadratic Equation

So far in this course, you have learned two algebraic methods to solve a quadratic equation of the form $ax^2 + bx + c = 0$.

One of these methods, the Zero Product Property, requires the equation to be a product of factors that equal zero. In this case, the quadratic equation must be factored, as shown in Example 1 below. Another strategy uses the Quadratic Formula, as demonstrated in Example 2 below. Notice that each strategy results in the same answer.

Example 1: Solve $3x^2 + x - 14 = 0$ for x using the Zero Product Property.

Solution: First, factor the quadratic so it is written as a product: $(3x + 7)(x - 2) = 0$. The Zero Product Property states that if the product of two terms is 0, then at least one of the factors must be 0. Thus, $3x + 7 = 0$ or $x - 2 = 0$.

Solving these equations for x reveals that $x = -\frac{7}{3}$ or that $x = 2$.

Example 2: Solve $3x^2 + x - 14 = 0$ for x using the Quadratic Formula $x = \frac{-b \pm \sqrt{b^2 - 4ac}}{2a}$.

Solution: First, identify a, b, and c. a equals the number of x^2-terms, b equals the number of x terms, while c equals the constant. For $3x^2 + x - 14 = 0$, $a = 3$, $b = 1$, and $c = -14$. Substitute the values of a, b, and c into the Quadratic Formula and evaluate the expression twice: once with addition and once with subtraction. Examine this method below:

$$x = \frac{-1 + \sqrt{1^2 - 4(3)(-14)}}{2 \cdot 3} \qquad x = \frac{-1 - \sqrt{1^2 - 4(3)(-14)}}{2 \cdot 3}$$

$$= \frac{-1 + \sqrt{169}}{6} \qquad\qquad = \frac{-1 - \sqrt{169}}{6}$$

$$= \frac{-1 + 13}{6} \qquad \text{or} \qquad = \frac{-1 - 13}{6}$$

$$= \frac{12}{6} \qquad\qquad\qquad = \frac{-14}{6}$$

$$= 2 \qquad\qquad\qquad = -\frac{7}{3}$$

8*118.   Write and solve an equation (or system of equations) for the situation described below. Define your variable(s) and write your solution as a sentence.

Daria has 18 coins that are all nickels and quarters. The number of nickels is 3 more than twice the number of quarters. If she has $1.90 in total, how many nickels does Daria have?

8*119.   Solve the following quadratic equations using any method.

   a. $10000x^2 - 64 = 0$ b. $9x^2 - 8 = -34x$

   c. $2x^2 - 4x + 7 = 0$ d. $0.2x + 3.2x^2 - 5 = 0$

8*120.   Find a rule that represents the number of tiles in Figure x for the tile pattern below.

     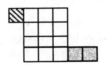   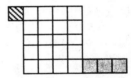

   Figure 1   Figure 2   Figure 3

8*121.   Solve the equations below for x. Check your solutions.

   a. $3x^2 + 3x = 6 + 3x^2$ b. $\frac{5}{x} = \frac{1}{3}$

   c. $5 - (2x - 3) = -3x + 6$ d. $6(x - 3) + 2x = 4(2x + 1) - 22$

8*122.   **Multiple Choice:** Which line below is perpendicular to the line $2x - 5y = 3$?

   a. $2x + 5y = 7$ b. $-2x + 5y = 4$ c. $5x - 2y = -1$ d. $5x + 2y = 3$

8*123.   Line L passes through the points (-44, 42) and (-31, 94) while line M has the rule $y = 6 + 3x$. Which line is steeper? Support your answer.

① TEAM BRAINSTORM

With your team, brainstorm a list for each of the following topics. Be as detailed as you can. How long can you make your list? Challenge yourselves.

Topics:	What have we studied in this chapter? What ideas and words were important in what we learned? Remember to be as detailed as you can.
Ways of Thinking:	What Ways of Thinking have we used in this chapter? When did we use them?
Connections:	What topics, ideas, and words that we learned *before* this chapter are connected to the new ideas in this chapter? Again, make your list as long as you can.

Be prepared to share your team's ideas with the class.

② MAKING CONNECTIONS

The following is a list of all the key words in this chapter. The words that appear in bold are new to this chapter. Make sure that you are familiar with all of these words.

binomial (p. 328)	**factor (p. 328)**	generic rectangle
graph	**monomial (p. 328)**	parabola
product	**quadratic equation (p. 346, 364)**	
Quadratic Formula (p. 356)	**root (p. 343, 346)**	solution
standard form for quadratics (p. 334)	sum	**symmetry (p. 340)**
trinomial (p. 328)	**vertex (p. 339)**	x-intercept
$x \rightarrow y$ table	y-intercept	

Zero Product Property (p. 347, 364)

Make a concept map showing all of the **connections** you can find between the key words and ideas listed above. For each key word or idea, sketch an example. Label each connection with a phrase explaining how the ideas are related. While you are making your map, you may think of related ideas that are not listed above. Be sure to include these ideas in your concept map.

③ SUMMARIZING MY UNDERSTANDING

This section gives you an opportunity to show what you know about one or more topics or ideas. Your teacher will give you directions for exactly how to do this, possibly providing you with a "GO" page to work on. The "GO" stands for "Graphic Organizer," a tool you can use to organize your thoughts and communicate your ideas clearly.

④ WHERE AM I?

This section will help you evaluate which types of problems you feel comfortable with and which you need more help with. Even if your teacher does not assign this section, it is a good idea to try the problems and find out for yourself what you know and what you need to work on.

Solve each problem as completely as you can. The table at the end of the closure section has answers to these problems. It also tells you where you can find additional help and practice on problems like these.

CL 8*1.   For the graph of the line at right:

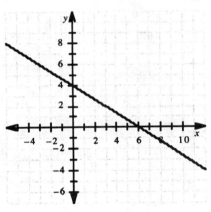

   a.   find the slope.

   b.   find the y-intercept.

   c.   find the equation.

   d.   find the equation of a line perpendicular to this one that passes through $(0,7)$.

CL 8*2.   Factor and use the Zero Product Property to find the roots of the following quadratic equations:

   a. $y = x^2 - 7x + 12$ b. $y = 6x^2 - 23x + 20$

   c. $y = x^2 - 9$ d. $y = x^2 + 12x + 36$

CL 8*3.   Use the Quadratic Formula to solve these equations.

   a. $0 = x^2 - 7x + 3$ b. $3x^2 + 5x + 1 = 0$

CL 8*4.   Use the graph to answer the questions below.

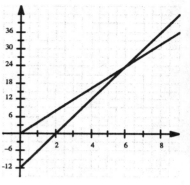

      a.   One of these lines represents Fengxian, and one represents Wai Teng. Write an equation for each girl's line.

      b.   The two girls are riding bikes. How fast does each ride?

      c.   When do Fengxian and Wai Teng meet? At that point, how far are they from school?

CL 8*5.   Factor completely:

      a. $3x^2 + 21x + 30$ b. $6x^2 + xy - 2y^2$

      c. $7x^2 - 63$

CL 8*6.   Simplify using the order of operations:

      a. $6 - 2(2^2 + 5) + \frac{3+7}{8-3} \div 2$ b. $\left(\frac{4}{2}\right)^2 - (-3 - 9)\left(7 - \frac{14}{2}\right) - 4$

CL 8*7.   Find the coordinates of the y-intercept, x-intercepts, and vertex of $y = x^2 - 2x - 15$. Show all the work that you do to find these points.

CL 8*8.   Solve for x using the method of your choice.

      a. $0 = 2x^2 - 5x - 33$ b. $0 = 3x^2 - 4x - 1$

CL 8*9.   Quinn started off with twice as much candy as Denali, but then he ate 4 pieces. When Quinn and Denali put their candy together, they now have a total of 50 pieces. How many pieces of candy did Denali start with?

CL 8*10.   Check your answers to each problem above using the table at the end of the closure section. Which problems did you feel confident about? Which problems were difficult? Use the table to make a list of topics you need help with and a list of topics you need to practice more.

⑤ HOW AM I THINKING?

This course emphasizes the following five Ways of Thinking:

- Reversing processes (going in both directions)
- Justifying (explaining why)
- Generalizing (showing how it works for all cases)
- Making Connections (showing how it fits in with other ideas)
- Applying and/or extending our knowledge (thinking about how we use it or where it can go)

Choose three of these ways of thinking that you remember using while working in this chapter. For each Way of Thinking that you choose, show and explain where you used it and how you used it. Describe why thinking in this way helped you solve a particular problem or understand something new. (For instance, explain why we wanted to generalize in this particular case or why it was useful to see these particular connections.) Be sure to include examples to demonstrate your thinking.

Problem	Solution	Need Help?	More Practice
CL 8*1	a. $m = \frac{-2}{3}$ b. y-int: 4 c. $y = -\frac{2}{3}x + 4$ d. $y = \frac{3}{2}x + 7$	MN p. 288, MN p. 295, MN p. 307	8*9, 8*17, 8*18, 8*21, 8*31, 8*38, 8*46, 8*48, 8*59, 8*83, 8*88, 8*101, 8*122, 8*123
CL 8*2	a. 4 and 3 b. −3 and 3 c. $\frac{5}{2}$ and $\frac{4}{3}$ d. -6	MN p. 337, 8*13, 8*62	8*6, 8*7, 8*12, 8*15, 8*16, 8*22, 8*23, 8*29, 8*33, 8*34, 8*37, 8*50
CL 8*3	a. $x = \frac{7 \pm \sqrt{37}}{2}$ or $x \approx 6.54$ or 0.46 b. $x = \frac{-5 \pm \sqrt{13}}{6}$ or $x \approx -0.23$ or -1.43	8*94, MN p. 357	8*45, 8*82, 8*96, 8*105, 8*106, 8*108, 8*109

Problem	Solution	Need Help?	More Practice
CL 8*4	a. Fengxian: $y = 4x$ Wai Teng: $y = 6(x - 2)$ b. Fengxian rides at 6 miles per hour and Wai Teng rides at 4 miles per hour. c. Fengxian and Wai Teng meet after 6 hours. At that point, they are 6 miles from school.	MN p. 244, MN p. 275	8*19, 8*30, 8*39, 8*60
CL 8*5	a. $3(x + 2)(x + 5)$ b. $(3x + 2y)(2x - y)$ c. $7(x + 3)(x - 3)$	MN p. 337, 8*35	8*15, 8*16, 8*22, 8*36, 8*71
CL 8*6	a. -11 b. 0	MN p. 58	3*14, 3*28
CL 8*7	y-int -15 x-int 5 and -3 vertex $(1, -16)$	Lesson 8.2.1, Lesson 8.2.2	8*10, 8*17, 8*18, 8*40, 8*42, 8*47, 8*52, 8*56, 8*58, 8*61, 8*65, 8*66, 8*80, 8*84, 8*87, 8*110, 8*117
CL 8*8	a. $x = \frac{11}{2} \, or -3$ b. $x = \frac{2 \pm \sqrt{7}}{3} \, or \ x \approx 1.55 \, or -0.22$	MN P.347, 8*94	8*32, 8*64, 8*67, 8*68, 8*70, 8*73, 8*74, 8*79, 8*90
CL 8*9	Denali has 18 pieces of candy.	MN P. 228, 6*3, 6*5	8*27, 8*41, 8*111, 8*118, 8*121

CHAPTER 9

Inequalities

So far in this course you have focused on what you can determine when two expressions are equal. By using what you know about balancing equations, you can now solve linear and quadratic equations for a given variable.

However, what if the two expressions are not equal? In fact, if we know that one expression is always larger than the other, what does that tell us about the variable? In this chapter you will learn how to deal with these types of relationships, called *inequalities*, and will develop ways to represent solutions to inequalities both algebraically and graphically.

In addition, you will extend your ability to solve word problems by examining how to represent words with equations in *mathematical sentences*.

Guiding Questions

Think about these questions throughout this chapter:

How can I represent it algebraically?

How can I solve it?

What is a solution?

What is the connection?

In this chapter, you will learn:

➤ How to write an algebraic sentence to represent a word problem.

➤ How to solve linear inequalities and represent the solutions on a number line.

➤ How to represent the solutions of linear and nonlinear inequalities with two variables on a graph.

➤ How to graph a system of inequalities.

Chapter Outline

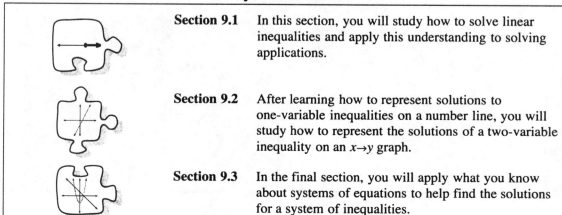

Section 9.1 In this section, you will study how to solve linear inequalities and apply this understanding to solving applications.

Section 9.2 After learning how to represent solutions to one-variable inequalities on a number line, you will study how to represent the solutions of a two-variable inequality on an $x \rightarrow y$ graph.

Section 9.3 In the final section, you will apply what you know about systems of equations to help find the solutions for a system of inequalities.

9.1.1 What if the quantities aren't equal?

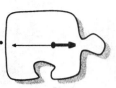

Solving Linear, 1-Variable Inequalities

In this course, you have developed a variety of skills to find solutions to different kinds of equations. Now you will **apply** these equation-solving skills to solve inequalities.

9*1.   As a class, create a human number line for each of the following mathematical sentences. You will be assigned a number to represent on the number line. When your number makes the equation or inequality true, stand up to show that your number is a solution. If your number does not make the equation or inequality true, remain seated.

a. $x \geq -2$ b. $x \leq 1$ c. $x = 3$ d. $x \geq 0$

e. $x = -2$ f. $-1 \leq x \leq 4$ g. $x^2 \geq 4$ h. $x < -3$

9*2.   Based on your observations from problem 9*1, discuss the following questions with your team. Be prepared to share your responses with the class.

a.   Compare the solutions to an inequality (like $x \geq -2$) with that of an equation (like $x = 3$)? What is different? What causes this to happen?

b.   How many solutions does an inequality such as $x \leq 1$ have?

c.   How is the result of $-1 \leq x \leq 4$ different from the other inequalities? What about the result of $x^2 \geq 4$?

9*3.   Write an inequality that represents the solutions on the number lines below.

a.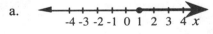

b.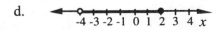

c.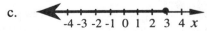

d.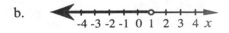

9*4.   SOLUTIONS OF A LINEAR INEQUALITY

With your study team, find at least **five** x-values that make the inequality below true:

$$2x - 5 \geq 3$$

a.   How many solutions are there?

b.   What is the smallest solution for x? This point is called a **boundary point**.

c.   What is the significance of the boundary point? What is its relationship with the inequality $2x - 5 \geq 3$?

d.   Write an inequality that represents the solutions for x. On a number line, highlight the solutions for x. Be ready to share your number line with the class.

9*5.   SOLVING LINEAR INEQUALITIES WITH ONE VARIABLE

Analyze the process to solve an inequality, such as $3 - 2x < 1$, by addressing the questions below.

a.   The key point to start with is the **boundary point**. How can you quickly solve for this point? Once you have determined your strategy, find the boundary point for $3 - 2x < 1$.

b.   Decide if the boundary point is part of the solution to the inequality or not. If it is part of the solution, indicate this on a number line with a solid point. If it is not a solution, show this by using an **unfilled** circle as a boundary.

c.   Finally, to determine on which side of the boundary the solutions lie, choose a point to test in the inequality. If the point **is** a solution, then all points on that side of the boundary are part of the solution. If the point is not a solution, what does that tell you about the solutions? Write your solutions to $3 - 2x < 1$ as an inequality and represent the solutions on a number line.

9*6.   With your study team, find all the solutions for the inequality $3x + 1 < 7$. Decide how to represent these solutions on a number line and be prepared to **justify** your decisions with the class.

METHODS AND MEANINGS

Inequality Symbols

Just as mathematics uses the symbol "=" to represent that two quantities are equal, it also uses the symbols at right when describing the relationships between quantities that are not necessarily equal. Review the inequality symbols at right. When graphing, a solid point indicates the value is a solution. An unfilled circle is not part of the solution.

<   less than
≤   less than or equal to
>   more than
≥   more than or equal to

9*7.   Solve the problem below by writing and solving an equation. A Guess and Check table may help you write the equation. Be sure to define your variable.

There are a total of 122 countries in Africa, Europe, and North America (as of 2003). Europe has twice as many countries as North America, and Africa has seven more than Europe. How many countries are in each of these three continents? Write an equation and solve it to answer this question.

9*8.   Solve each of the following inequalities for the given variable. Represent your solutions on a number line.

a. $2(3p+1) > -4$ b. $9k - 2 < 3k + 10$ c. $5 - k \geq 4$

9*9.   Solve the following quadratic equations. Check your solutions, if possible.

a. $2k^2 + k - 6 = 0$ b. $m^2 = 9$

c. $w(2w + 8) = 24$ d. $3n^2 - 4n = 5$

9*10.   Identify the statements below as sometimes true, always true, or never true.

	less than
<	less than
≤	less than or equal to
>	more than
≥	more than or equal to

a. $-4 \leq 9$ b. $x < 1$ c. $-5 > -2$

d. $3x + 5 = 2$ e. $61 = 61$ f. $|x| = -3$

9*11.   Assuming that x does not equal zero, what is $\frac{x}{x}$? Explain how you know.

9*12.   Find the point(s) of intersection of the system of equations at right. Show all your work.

$$y = 5x - 22$$
$$y = x^2 - 6x + 8$$

9*13.   Robbie builds model rockets. One day he sets up a rocket, backs away from the launch pad, and then shoots the rocket off into space. The rocket's path is represented by the equation $y = -10x^2 + 130x - 400$, where y is the height in meters off the ground and x is the horizontal distance in meters from Robbie.

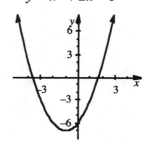

a.   Use either the Zero Product Property or the Quadratic Formula to find the x-intercepts of the path of Robbie's rocket. What do the x-intercepts tell us?

b.   When Robbie's rocket lands, how far is it from the launch pad?

9*14.   For each parabola graphed below, visually estimate the x-intercepts. Then use the Quadratic Formula to confirm your estimates.

a. $y = x^2 - 5x + 3$

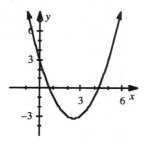

b. $y = x^2 + 2x - 6$

9.1.2 How can we use inequalities?

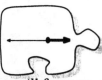

In Lesson 9.1.1 you learned how to solve inequalities with one variable. Today we will focus on special inequalities and learn how we can use inequalities to solve application problems.

9*15. Review what you learned in Lesson 9.1.1 to solve the inequalities below. Represent your solutions on a number line.

a. $x - 7 < -2$

b. $3m + 2 \le 8m - 8$

c. $\frac{2}{3}p - 2 > -4$

d. $2 - 3(x - 1) \ge x - 7$

e. $9k - 4 + 1 \le 2k - 3 + 7k$

f. $3y + 1 < 3y + 1$

9*16. THE UNITED NATIONS

At the end of this chapter your team will have the exciting responsibility to represent a country at a special meeting of the United Nations (the "U. N."). The U. N. needs your help preparing for future large-scale disasters. You will need to help find a solution that not only works best for the country you represent, but also accommodates the needs of each of the other countries. To prepare you for this task, this chapter will present daily problems to familiarize you with the important issues and concerns of other countries.

Start by writing and solving a system of equations to represent the problem below. Be sure to define your variables.

Turkey has a population of 66 million people and is made up almost entirely of two ethnic groups: Turks and Kurds. There are 4 times more Turks than Kurds. Write an equation and solve it to find out how many Kurds live in Turkey.

9*17. In 1912, Japan gave the United States several thousand flowering cherry trees as a symbol of friendship. Similarly, the nation of Cameroon is planning to give flowering Satta trees to other countries this year. When asked how to decide which Satta trees make good gifts, Cameroon's chief arborist explained,

"We plant Satta trees when they are 6 cm tall and they grow 9 cm every year. The trees only flower when they are taller than 150 cm."

It is very important that the trees they give flower this year! It would be considered an insult to receive a tree that did not bloom. Luckily, Cameroon has many groves of Satta trees from which to select its gifts. How old must the trees be so that they will flower within the year?

a. Discuss with your study team whether an inequality or an equation is appropriate for this situation. Be prepared to share your reasoning.

b. Write an appropriate mathematical sentence and solve it to determine how old the trees can be, so that they flower this year.

c. Later, the arborist added, "I almost forgot to tell you – when the trees become very old, they stop flowering. Make sure you choose trees that are no more than 240 cm tall!" Discuss with your team how you can use this additional information to make sure you choose trees that will flower. Be prepared to share your answer with the class.

Review & Preview

9*18.   Solve the inequalities below for the given variables. Represent your solutions on a number line.

   a. $3(2k-1)<9$

   b. $\frac{2p}{5}\le 6$

   c. $-2+8n>2$

   d. $7t-4\ge 2t-4$

9*19.   Use your graphing shortcuts to graph $y=-2x+3$. Identify the x- and y-intercepts.

9*20.   Find the equation of the line with slope $-\frac{3}{5}$ passing through the point (-6, 2).

9*21.   Use a generic rectangle to multiply $(x+2)(3x-5)$.

   a.   What is $(3x^2+x-10)\div(x+2)$? How do you know?

   b.   Likewise determine $(3x^2+x-10)\div(3x-5)$.

9*22.   Solve the quadratic equation below. Check your solutions with a calculator.

$$3x^2+2.5x=12.5$$

9*23.   Factor the expressions below completely, if possible.

   a. $4x^2-20x+25$

   b. $x^2+11x-2$

   c. $3x^2-12x$

   d. $10x^2-35x-20$

9.2.1 How can we graph an inequality with 2 variables?

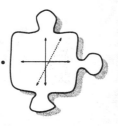

Graphing 2-Variable Inequalities

9*24.   EXAMINING THE SOLUTIONS OF A LINEAR EQUATION

Find your graph of $y = -2x + 3$ from problem 9*19. Compare your graph with the poster graph provided by your teacher.

a.   Is the point (-1, 5) a solution of the equation $y = -2x + 3$? How can you tell by looking at the graph? How can you tell by using the equation?

b.   Is the point (2, -1) a solution? What about the point (0, 0)? **Justify** each conclusion with the graph and the equation.

c.   What determines if a point lies on the line or not? What is the difference between the points on the line and those that are not on the line?

9*25.   GRAPHING A LINEAR INEQUALITY

In problem 9*24, you found that the points on the line are the **only** points that make the equation $y = -2x + 3$ true. But what if we want to graph the solutions for the inequality $y \geq -2x + 3$? How will that graph differ from $y = -2x + 3$? Consider this question as you follow the steps below.

a.   Your team will be given a list of points to test in the inequality $y \geq -2x + 3$. For each point that makes the inequality true, place a sticky dot on that point on the class graph.

b.   Now examine the solutions shown on the graph. With your team, discuss the questions below. Be ready to share your discoveries with the class.

•   Are there any points on the graph that you suspect are solutions but do not have a sticker?

•   Are there any stickers that you think may be misplaced? If so, verify these points so that you can have a complete graph of the solutions.

•   What about the points on the line? Are they all solutions to the inequality $y \geq -2x + 3$? Why or why not?

•   How many solutions are there?

•   Why are none of the solutions below the line?

9*26.   What else can we learn about solutions of linear inequalities? Think about this as you answer the questions below with your team.

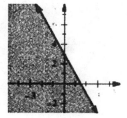

a.   What if the graph were shaded like the one at right? What inequality would correspond with this graph?

b.   Heidi asks, "What if I changed the inequality to be $y < -2x + 3$? Now what would the graph look like?" Discuss this with your teammates and decide how to best represent the solutions of $y < -2x + 3$. Be prepared to share your graph with the class.

9*27.   Graph the inequalities below on graph paper. For each inequality:

- Graph the boundary as either a solid or a dashed line.

- Shade the region that makes the inequality true.

a. $y > -\frac{1}{3}x - 1$ b. $y \leq 4x + 2$

c. $y < \frac{5}{2}x + 3$ d. $2x - y \leq 5$

9*28.   As a Learning Reflection, explain how to graph a linear inequality. Be sure to address the questions below. Title this entry "Graphing Linear Inequalities" and include today's date.

- How can you determine if the line is part of the solution or not?

- How can you determine which side of the line the solution belongs?

- What point(s) is (are) easiest to test?

- How many points do you need to test?

9*29.   Represent the solutions to the inequalities below on a number line.

a. $3x - 2 < 10$ b. $5x - 1 - 3x \geq 4x + 5$

c. $2(x + 2) > 10 - x$ d. $4(x - 3) + 5 \geq -7$

9*30.   Algeria has decided to take out an advertisement in
the U.N newspaper, *Liberty Daily*. The newspaper
charges a base fee of $1200. There is an additional
fee of $300 for every inch in height. If Algeria is
willing to spend any amount up to $2700, what
choices do they have for the height of the ad?

9*31.   Solve the problem below by writing and solving one or two equations. A Guess and
Check table may help you get started. Be sure to define your variable(s) and write your
solution as a sentence.

Rowan received 3 points for each question he answered correctly on Part 1 of a test and
2 points for each question he answered correctly on Part 2. If he answered 33 questions
correctly and received a total of 85 points, how many questions did he answer correctly
on Part 1?

9*32.   Line *m* has intercepts (-7, 0) and (0, -2).

a.   Find the equation of line *m*.

b.   Does the point (49, -16) also lie on line *m*? How do you know?

c.   Write the equation of a line that is perpendicular to line *m* and passes through the
point (6, -1).

9*33.   Find the point of intersection of the two functions below using any method. Describe
how you found your solution.

$$y = 2x + 9$$
$$y = x^2 - 2x - 3$$

9*34.   **Multiple Choice:** Which of the expressions below is a factor of $6m^2 + 7m - 5$?

a. $2m + 1$ b. $m + 5$ c. $2m - 5$ d. $3m + 5$

9.2.2 What if the inequality is not linear?

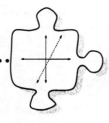

Graphing Linear and Non-linear Inequalities

In Lesson 9.2.1, you discovered that the solutions of a linear inequality with 2 variables can be represented by a shaded region on one side of the line. But what happens when the inequality is not linear? How can we graphically represent the solutions to an inequality that is quadratic or that includes an absolute value? Consider these questions as you complete the following problems with your study team.

9*35. Review what you learned about graphing inequalities in Lesson 9.2.1 by writing the inequality for the solution graphed at right. Be prepared to explain how you found your rule.

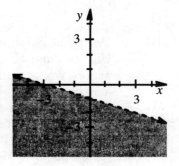

9*36. Graph the inequality below on graph paper.

$$y \geq -\tfrac{5}{3}x - 3$$

a. What is the minimum number of points you need to test in order to know which side of the line the solution falls?

b. Orville loves using the point $(0, 0)$ to test the inequality. Why is using this point so convenient?

c. Anita decided to use $(-3, 2)$ to test the inequality. Test the inequality with her point. Does this point help her decide which side to shade? Why or why not?

9*37. What if the inequality is non-linear? Decide with your team how to graph the inequality $y < x^2 - 4x + 3$ on graph paper. Your graphing shortcuts can help.

9*38.   With your team, graph the following inequalities on graph paper.

a. $y < -\frac{2}{3}x + 4$ b. $y > x^2$ c. $y \leq 4$

9*39.   FOREIGN AID

One of the purposes of the
United Nations is to have
nations work together to
help one another. Recently,
the members of the U. N.
decided to give grants to
poor countries to help
reduce poverty. However,
the United Nations only
has the resources to help
those countries in the
greatest need. Therefore,
it was decided that only
countries in which the number
of people in poverty is **more than** one-half of its total population would receive foreign
aid.

a.   Write an inequality that represents the criteria to receive foreign aid. Let x
represent the population and y represent the number of people in poverty.

b.   On the Resource Page provided by your teacher, find the graphs that show the
number of people in poverty per the population for each of the countries
requesting foreign aid. Carefully graph your inequality from part (a) on this data
graph. Which countries will receive foreign aid?

METHODS AND MEANINGS

Solving 1-variable Inequalities

To solve a 1-variable inequality, we first treat the problem as if it were an equality. The solution to the equality is called the **boundary point**. For example, $x = 12$ is the boundary point for the inequality $3 + 2(x - 5) \le 17$, as shown below.

Problem: $3 + 2(x - 5) \le 17$

First change the problem to an equality and solve for x:

$$3 + 2(x - 5) \le 17$$
$$3 + 2x - 10 = 17$$
$$2x - 7 = 17$$
$$2x = 24$$
$$x = 12$$

Since our original inequality **included** $x = 12$, we place our boundary point on our number line as a solid point. We then test one value on either side in the **original** inequality to determine which set of numbers makes the inequality true.

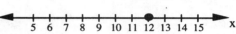

Test: $x = 8$	Test: $x = 15$
$3 + 2(8 - 5) \le 17$	$3 + 2(15 - 5) \le 17$
$3 + 2 \cdot 3 \le 17$	$3 + 2 \cdot 10 \le 17$
$3 + 6 \le 17$	$3 + 20 \le 17$
TRUE!	FALSE!

Therefore, the solution is $x \le 12$.

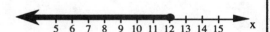

When the inequality is "<" or ">," the boundary point is **not** included in the answer. On a number line, this would be indicated with an open circle at 12.

9*40. **Multiple Choice:** Which of the expressions below is a factor of $6x^2 + 7x - 20$?

　　a.　　$3x - 4$　　　　b.　　$2x - 5$　　　　c.　　$3x + 4$　　　　d.　　$4x - 3$

9*41. **Multiple Choice:** Which of the following expressions is the product of $(4y - 3x)(2y + x)$?

　　a.　　$8y^2 - 2xy - 3x^2$　　　　　　　　b.　　$6y^2 - 2xy - 2x^2$

　　c.　　$8y^2 + 10xy - 3x^2$　　　　　　　d.　　$6y^2 - 2x$

9*42. Solve the following equations for x. Check your solution(s), if possible.

　　a.　　$\frac{3}{x} = 9$　　　　　　　　　　　b.　　$\sqrt{x} = 4$

　　c.　　$x^2 = 25$　　　　　　　　　　　d.　　$|x| + 4 = 7$

9*43. During a race, Bernie ran 9 meters every 4 seconds, while Barnaby ran 2 meters every second and got a 10 meter head start. If the race was 70 meters long, did Bernie ever catch up with Barnaby? If so, when? **Justify** your answer.

9*44. WHAT'S THE DIFFERENCE?

Examine the following situations in which we need to find the difference between two amounts.

　　a.　　Rocio has $298 saved in the bank, while Thomas has $314. What is the difference between their bank balances? How did you get your answer?

　　b.　　The temperature in Minneapolis on January 10 ranged between −23° and 19° Fahrenheit. What was the different between the high and low temperatures for this date? How did you get your answer?

　　c.　　Urban High School has 1850 students while Metro High School has 1490 students. What is the difference of their student populations?

　　d.　　Explain why these differences are all positive.

9*45. Find the roots of the parabola $y = 5x^2 + 7x - 6$ using **two different methods**. The answers from each method should match.

9.2.3 What's the difference?

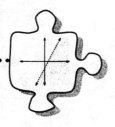

Introduction to Absolute Value

In the past few lessons, you learned what inequalities mean. You graphed linear and non-linear inequalities. Now you will learn a new operation and how you can use it to create new inequality graphs.

9*46.   ABSOLUTE VALUE OPERATION

Your teacher will present you with information about an operation called **absolute value.**

a.   Study the relationship between the number entered in the ( ) and the results shown. Write a statement describing this operation.

```
abs(-11)
                    11
abs(4)
                     4
abs(-100)
                   100
```

b.   Why would we ever need an absolute value?

9*47.   While some graphing calculators, like the one shown in problem 9*46, display the absolute value as "abs(-100) = 100", the written notation is $|-100| = 100$. This notation consists of two vertical lines on each side of the input value.

a.   The expression $|-3| + 1$ can be translated as "*Change –3 to a positive value and then add 1.*" Translate the expression $|-5+1| - 3$ and then find its value.

b.   Evaluate these expressions:

  i. $|-100| - 98$ *ii.* $5|2-8|$

  iii. $|-13| + |0|$ *iv.* $14 - |-10+3|$

c.   Now create your own expression using the absolute value that has a result of 10. Be creative and be ready to share your expression with the class.

9*48.   Mr. Guo is thinking of a number. When he takes the absolute value of his number, he gets 15. What can his number be? Is there more than one possible answer?

9*49.   Riley wants to know what an absolute value might look like on a graph.

   a.   Set up a table and graph $y = |x|$.

   b.   Describe for Riley what the graph looks like. Be as detailed as you can.

9*50.   Dorinae is confused. She is making a table for $y = |x + 1|$. She is trying to find y when $x = -3$, but she is not sure if she should find the absolute value first, or if she should first add one. Explain to Dorinae what she should do first.

9*51.   Graph the inequality $y < |2x - 1|$. Be ready to share your graph with the class.

Definition of Absolute Value

MATH NOTES

An **absolute value**, represented by two vertical bars, " | | ", determines the positive value of a number. Numerically, it represents a distance on a number line between the number and zero. Since a distance is always positive, the absolute value is always a positive value or zero.

For example, the number -3 is 3 units from 0, as shown on the number line at right. Therefore, the absolute value of -3 is 3. This is written $|-3| = 3$.

distance of 3

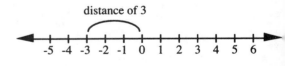

Likewise, the number 5 is 5 units from 0. The absolute value of 5 is 5, written $|5| = 5$.

distance of 5

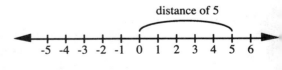

Algebra Connections: Chapter 9

9*52.   Brazil's rainforests currently cover about 1,400,000 square miles, but are becoming smaller every year because of deforestation. Realizing that the rainforests are a great resource, Brazil has decided to control how quickly the forests are destroyed.

In 50 years Brazil would like the rainforests to cover **more than** 1,200,000 square miles. If x represents the forest area that is destroyed each year, write and solve an inequality that would help determine acceptable values of x.

9*53.   Solve the following quadratic equations. Check your solutions, if possible.

a. $2k^2 + k - 6 = 0$ b. $m^2 = 9$

c. $w(2w + 8) = 24$ d. $3n^2 - 4n = 5$

9*54.   Clifford thinks that $x = 7$ is a solution to $3(x - 2) \leq 4$. Is he correct? Show why or why not.

9*55.   Graph the inequalities below on graph paper.

a. $y \leq -x + 5$ b. $y > \frac{2}{3}x - 1$

9*56.   Zachary has $718 in his bank account and automatically withdraws (subtracts) $14 every month to pay for his computer service. Christian has $212 in his bank account and deposits (adds) $32 each month from his newspaper delivery tips. When will they have the same amount of money in their bank accounts?

9*57.   Stacey is the star of the basketball team. She makes many baskets during each game and could break the record for her high school. The data for the first five games of this season is below.

Game Number	Number of Baskets
1	6
2	11
3	18
4	25
5	31

a.   Plot a graph with these data points.

b.   Draw a trend line for this data using two carefully selected points that best represent the data.

c.   Use the equation of your line to predict how many baskets Stacey will make by the end of the season if the season has 15 games.

9.3.1 How can we represent it?

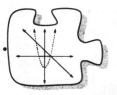

Systems of Inequalities

In Chapter 6 you learned that the solution to a system of equations is a point that makes both equations true, but what about the solution for a system of two inequalities? How can you represent these solutions on a graph? How many solutions can a system of inequalities have?

Consider these questions as you learn how to graph a system of inequalities.

9*58.   Find your graphs for problem 9*55.

    a.   Compare your solution graphs for $y \leq -x + 5$ and $y > \frac{2}{3}x - 1$ with those of your teammates. Correct any errors. Be sure to focus on whether or not the boundary line should be included in each graph.

    b.   Now consider the system of inequalities below. Which points are solutions to this system? That is, which points make **both** inequalities true?

$$y \leq -x + 5$$
$$y > \frac{2}{3}x - 1$$

    c.   If you have not done so already, verify your solution region from part (b) algebraically, by substituting the coordinates of a point from your solution region into each inequality.

    d.   How can you be sure this region is the only set of points that makes both inequalities true?

9*59.   Draw a graph of the region satisfying both inequalities at right. Start by graphing the boundary lines and then test points to find the region that makes both inequalities true.

$$y < x + 2$$
$$y \leq 10 - \frac{3}{4}x$$

9*60.   HOW MANY REGIONS?

When graphing the systems of inequalities below, Reyna started with the boundary graph of each inequality shown at right.

$$y \leq x^2 - x - 6$$
$$y > \frac{2}{3}x$$

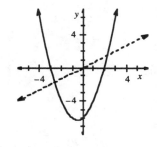

Continued on next page →

9*60.   *Continued from previous page*

   a.   Why is the line graphed with a dashed line while the
        parabola is not?

   b.   Find a copy of Reyna's graph on the Resource Page distributed by your teacher.
        How many possible solution regions are there? Carefully count each region with
        your teammates.

   c.   Pick a point in each region and test it in the system of inequalities. Shade any
        regions that contain solutions to both inequalities. How many regions make up
        the solution to this system?

   d.   Why is (0, 0) not a good point to use to test for this solution?

9*61.   How does changing the inequality affect the solution graph? Notice that each system
          of inequalities below uses the same boundary graphs as Reyna's graph from problem
          9*59. However, notice that this time the inequalities are slightly altered.

          With your teammates, devise a method to determine which region (or regions) are
          solutions for each system. Shade the appropriate regions on your Resource Page.

   a. $y \geq x^2 - x - 6$ b. $y \geq x^2 - x - 6$ c. $y \leq x^2 - x - 6$
        $y > \frac{2}{3}x$ $y < \frac{2}{3}x$ $y < \frac{2}{3}x$

9*62.   The United Nations asked every nation to write a system of inequalities that best
          approximates their country's shape (the U.N. thinks this will help find each country's
          area). Honduras sent in their inequalities by fax, but
          some of the information is unreadable. With your
          study team, determine the missing parts of the
          inequalities and rewrite them on your paper.

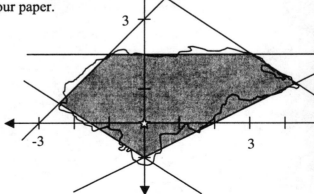

   $y \quad x+3$ $y \geq \frac{1}{2}x-$

   $\quad 2$ $y \quad -\frac{2}{3}x+4$

   $y \quad -\frac{2}{3}x-1$

METHODS AND **M**EANINGS

Graphing Inequalities with 2 Variables

To graph an inequality with two variables, first graph the boundary line or curve. If the inequality does not include an equality (such as > or <), then the graph of the boundary is dashed to indicate that it is not included in the solution. Otherwise, the boundary is a solid line or curve.

Once the boundary is graphed, choose a point that does not lie on the boundary to test in the inequality. If that point makes the inequality true, then the entire region in which that point lies is a solution. Examine the two examples below.

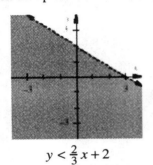

$y < \frac{2}{3}x + 2$

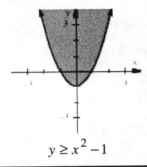

$y \geq x^2 - 1$

Review & Preview

9*63.   Match each graph below with the correct inequality.

a. $y > -x + 2$ b. $y < 2x - 3$ c. $y \geq \frac{1}{2}x$ d. $y \leq -\frac{2}{3}x + 2$

1)

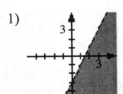

2

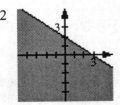

3)

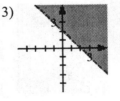

4

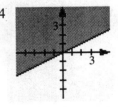

9*64.   Solve each inequality below. Represent the solutions on number lines.

a. $7x - 2 < 3 + 2x$

b. $\frac{1}{3}x \geq 2$

c. $3(2m - 1) - 5m \leq -1$

d. $2k + 3 \leq 2k + 1$

9*65. Which of the following expressions are equal to 1? (Note: More than one expression may be equal to one!)

a. $\dfrac{114}{114}$ b. $\dfrac{2}{3} \cdot \dfrac{3}{2}$ c. $\dfrac{m+4}{m+4}$ d. $\dfrac{p^2}{p \cdot p}$

9*66. Factor the following quadratics completely.

a. $5x^2 + 13x - 6$ b. $6t^2 - 26t + 8$ c. $6x^2 - 24$

9*67. When a family with two adults and three children bought tickets for a movie, they paid a total of $27.75. The next family in line, with two children and three adults, paid $32.25 for the same movie. Find the adult and child ticket prices by writing a system of equations with two variables.

9*68. **Multiple Choice:** Which of the points below is a solution of $y < |x - 3|$?

a. (2, 1)   b. (-4, 5)   c. (-2, 8)   d. (0, 3)

9.3.2 How can I apply it?

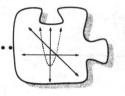

More Systems of Inequalities

9*69. Review what you learned about systems of inequalities in Lesson 9.3.1 by graphing the system of inequalities below on graph paper. Carefully shade the region of points that make **both** inequalities true.

$$y \le |x| + 4$$
$$-x + 4y \ge 4$$

9*70. Notice that each system of inequalities below contains the same boundary lines. On graph paper, graph the boundaries for each system and work with your teammates to decide which region is the solution, if a solution exists. Be ready to share your solution with the class.

a. $y \le \dfrac{2}{3}x + 3$
    $y \ge \dfrac{2}{3}x$

b. $y \le \dfrac{2}{3}x + 3$
    $y \le \dfrac{2}{3}x$

c. $y \ge \dfrac{2}{3}x + 3$
    $y \le \dfrac{2}{3}x$

9*71.   SEARCH & RESCUE

"I'm completely lost... water everywhere I can see... both engines have failed...Wait! I see land. I'm going to try to land. I think it's..."

Those were the last words heard from Harold in his hot-air balloon. The last time the balloon showed up on radar, it was near the Solomon Islands in the Pacific Ocean.

Your Task: Your team must determine where to send the search and rescue teams! Use the following reports along with the map on the Resource Page and look carefully for information that will help you draw boundary lines. Write a system of inequalities to give to the search and rescue team. Be sure to identify the probable landing site on the map.

Pilot's Report from a nearby airplane:

"We were on our way from Australia, when we saw a hot-air balloon sinking rapidly. I am certain that it crashed south of our flight path. When we left Australia, we traveled 2000 km north for every 3000 km east that we flew."

Basic Facts of the Case:

The balloon departed from the airport at the very northern tip of the Philippines. The flight was supposed to follow a straight path **directly** to an airport in French Polynesia.

The balloon's last known location was at (-1000, 1000) near the Solomon Islands.

Phone Call Received today:

"I was a passenger on a flight that flew directly from French Polynesia to Indonesia. I was looking out my window when I saw a huge splash in the ocean to the north of where we were flying."

9*72.   As a Learning Reflection, describe your method for graphing systems of inequalities for a student who has missed class for the last couple of days. Be sure to include examples and important details. Title this entry "Graphing Systems of Inequalities" and include today's date.

9*73.   Graph and shade the solution for the inequality below.

$$y < x^2 + 2x - 8$$

9*74.   Graph and shade the solution for the system of inequalities below.

$$y \geq \tfrac{3}{4}x - 2$$
$$y < -\tfrac{1}{2}x + 3$$

9*75.   Write the inequality that represents the *x*-values highlighted on the number line below.

a.    b.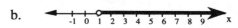

c.    d.

9*76.   For the Spring Festival, the Math Club is selling rulers for $1 and compasses for $2.50.

   a.   While the club would like to sell as many items as they can to raise funds, they need to make at least $15.00 to break even. Write an inequality to represent this situation. Let *r* = the number of rulers sold and *c* = the number of compasses sold.

   b.   School rules state that the club can only sell 25 items for the festival. Write an inequality for this constraint (limitation).

   c.   Graph these inequalities on the same set of axes. Find the region of points that are solutions to each of them. Can this region fall below the *x*-axis or to the left of the *y*-axis? Why or why not?

   d.   What do the points in the solution region represent?

9*77.   **Multiple Choice:** Which equation below is perpendicular to the line $y = \tfrac{1}{3}x + 7$?

   a. $x + 3y = 4$ b. $x - 3y = 4$ c. $3x + y = 4$ d. $3x - y = 4$

9.3.3 How can we use inequalities to solve problems?

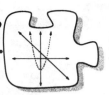

Applying Inequalities to Solve Problems

Today you will pull together all of the mathematics you have studied in this chapter and solve an important application problem.

9*78.   UNITED NATIONS TO THE RESCUE

As a representative of your country, you have been sent the following letter and given the following task:

> *Dear Representative to the United Nations:*
>
> *A critical matter has come to the attention of the United Nations. In the past, when a catastrophe struck a part of the world, the U. N. gathered supplies to give to people in need. Unfortunately, because the U. N. had to collect supplies from each country at the time of the catastrophe, it was always quite a few days before the supplies could be sent to the areas that needed them the most.*
>
> *A recommendation has come before the U. N. to create a supply of food and medicine packages for future emergencies. Each food package will be able to feed several hundred people while each medicine package will supply one first aid station. I am asking each country to donate the same number of packages, so that everyone shares the burden equally.*
>
> *I am asking each country to determine how many food and medicine packages they are able to give. You will present your findings at today's United Nations meeting. Please be certain to use the information that your country's Budget Committee has prepared in order to help you decide how many packages you can afford.*
>
> *Best of luck, and may our efforts make our world a better place!*
>
> *Sincerely,*
>
> *The Secretary General of the United Nations*

After consulting with your country's budget committee, your teacher will supply you with some information that will help decide how many food and medicine packets your country can afford.

Continued on next page →

9*78.   *Continued from previous page*

Your Task: In order to communicate your country's budget constraints, write an inequality expressing how many food and medicine packages your country is able to give. Let x equal the number of food packages and y equal the number of medicine packages.

On the Resource Page provided by your teacher, graph the solution region representing the number of medicine and food packets that can be donated by your country. Be prepared to share your graph with the other countries of the United Nations.

9*79.   As a member of the United Nations, you must consider each of the following proposals. In each case, assume that the United Nations would like to receive as many emergency supplies as possible, while still having each nation give equally.

   a.   One proposal is that each country gives 185 medicine packages. How many food packages should the United Nations require from each country in this case? Explain how you made your decision.

   b.   Another proposal is to get the largest number of medicine packages possible. What's the largest number of medicine packages that each country can offer? How did you find your answer?

9*80.   EXTENSION

A last-minute proposal suggests balancing the number of food and medicine supplies. For instance, if a country gives 150 food packages, then they would also give 150 medicine packages. How many food and medicine packages should the United Nations require from each country in this case? Explain how you determined your solution.

9*81.   While setting up a mathematical sentence to solve a problem, Paulina and Aliya came up with the equations below. Since they did not look alike, they both turned to you for help.

$$\text{Paulina: } 4x + 2y = 6$$

$$\text{Aliya: } 12x + 6y = 18$$

   a.   Are these equations equivalent? That is, will the graph of each line be the same? Explain how you know.

   b.   Find another equation that is equivalent to both of these. How did you find your equation?

9*82.   Get ready to conserve! Your town has decided to
          "Think globally, act locally!" by limiting the amount
          of trash thrown out each month. Your town, which
          has 3280 homes, has asked each household to keep
          track of how many pounds of trash they produce
          during a month. In addition, the town council has
          found that other sources of trash, such as local
          businesses, combine to create 1500 lbs of trash each
          month. If the town has a goal of creating **less than** 50,000 lbs of trash, how much trash
          should a household aim to produce? Write an inequality for this situation and solve it.

9*83.   Solve the following inequalities for the given variable and represent the solutions on a
          number line.

          a. $2 < 2m - 8$ b. $\frac{1}{3}x - 1 \le -3$

          c. $5(2x - 8) + 24 > 3(4 + 2x)$ d. $5 + 2k < k - 2 + k$

9*84.   Graph the system of inequalities below.

          $$y \ge x(x - 4)$$
          $$y < x$$

          a.   Carefully shade the solution region.

          b.   Is (0, 0) a solution to this system? How can you tell?

9*85.   Solve the quadratic equation below **twice**, once using the Zero Product Property and
          once using the Quadratic Formula. Verify that the solutions from both methods are the
          same.

          $$2x^2 - 19x + 9 = 0$$

9*86.   Read the following problem. Then decide which system of equations below can
          represent this situation.

          The length of a rectangle is 4 units longer than twice its width. If the area is 126 square
          units, find the length and width.

          a. $w = 2l + 4$ b. $l = 2w + 4$ c. $w = 2l + 4$ d. $l = 2w + 4$
                 $wl = 126$ $l + w = 126$ $l + w = 126$ $wl = 126$

① TEAM BRAINSTORM

With your team, brainstorm a list for each of the following topics. Be as detailed as you can. How long can you make your list? Challenge yourselves.

Topics: What have we studied in this chapter? What ideas and words were important in what we learned? Remember to be as detailed as you can.

Ways of Thinking: What ways of thinking have we used in this chapter? When did we use them?

Connections: What topics, ideas, and words learned *before* this chapter are **connected** to the new ideas in this chapter? Again, make your list as long as you can.

Be prepared to share your team's ideas with the class.

② MAKING CONNECTIONS

The following is a list of all of the key words in this chapter. The words that appear in bold are new to this chapter. Make sure that you are familiar with all of these words.

absolute value (p. 388)	**boundary (p. 385)**	coordinates
equation	graph	**inequality (p. 375)**
number line (p. 385)	**region (p. 393)**	solution
system of inequalities (p. 391)		

Make a concept map showing all of the **connections** you can find between the key words and ideas listed above. For each key word or idea, sketch an example. Label each connection with a phrase explaining how the ideas are related. While you are making your map, you may think of related ideas that are not listed above. Be sure to include these ideas in your concept map.

③ SUMMARIZING MY UNDERSTANDING

This section gives you an opportunity to show what you know about one or more topics or ideas. Your teacher will give you directions for exactly how to do this.

④ WHERE AM I?

This section will help you evaluate which types of problems you feel comfortable with and which ones you need more help with. Even if your teacher does not assign this section, it is a good idea to try the problems and find out for yourself what you know and what you need to work on.

Solve each problem as completely as you can. The table at the end of the closure section has answers to these problems. It also tells you where you can find additional help and practice on problems like these.

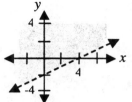

CL 9*1.   Write an inequality that represents the graph at right:

CL 9*2.   Find the equation of the line passing through the points $(-3, 13)$ and $(4, -1)$.

CL 9*3.   Is the point $(0, 4)$ a solution to the system of inequalities at right? **Justify** your answer.

$$y \leq -3x + 4$$
$$y > x^2 + 3x - 2$$

CL 9*4.   Factor these quadratic expressions completely.

a. $2x^3 + 8xy$

b. $-3x^2 + 23x - 14$

c. $2x^2 - 5x + 4$

d. $6x^2 + 10x - 24$

CL 9*5.   The Oakland SPCA has 14 kittens in one of its kitten rooms. Together, they eat 10 cups of food each day. If there is a total of 86 kittens in the whole Oakland SPCA, approximately how many cups of kitten food does the SPCA need each day?

CL 9*6.   Solve each inequality below for the given variable. Then represent each solution on a number line.

a. $4x - 3 \geq 9$

b. $3(t + 4) < 5$

c. $\frac{2y}{7} < 8$

d. $5x + 4 > -3(x - 8)$

CL 9*7.   Brian was holding a ballroom dance. He wanted to make sure girls would come, so he charged boys $5 to get in but girls only $3. The 45 people who came paid a total of $175. How many girls came to the dance?

CL 9*8.   Solve these quadratic equations using any method.

a. $0 = 3x^2 + 4x - 7$

b. $x^2 - 3x + 18 = 0$

CL 9*9.   Graph this system of inequalities:

$$y < x^2$$
$$y \geq x + 2$$

CL 9*10. Write equations for each of the lines depicted on the graph at right.

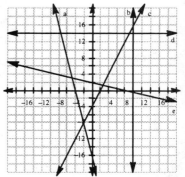

CL 9*11. Lew says to his granddaughter Audrey, "Even if you tripled your age and added 9, you still wouldn't be as old as me." Lew is 60 years old. Write and solve an inequality to determine the possible ages Audrey could be.

CL 9*12. Graph each of these inequalities on a separate graph:

    a. $y \le -\frac{1}{2} + 3$ b. $y > -x^2 + 2x + 8$ c. $y \ge |x + 2|$

CL 9*13. The hare leaps 500 centimeters every 20 seconds. The tortoise crawls 250 centimeters every 50 seconds, but gets a 1000 centimeter head start. Use any method you know to determine how long it takes the hare to catch the tortoise.

CL 9*14. Check your answers to each problem above using the table at the end of the closure section. Which problems did you feel confident about? Which problems were hard? Use the table to make a list of topics you need help on and a list of topics you need to practice more.

⑤ HOW AM I THINKING?

This course emphasizes the following five ways of thinking:

- Reversing processes (going in both directions)
- Justifying (explaining why)
- Generalizing (showing how it works for all cases)
- Making Connections (showing how it fits in with other ideas)
- Applying and/or extending our knowledge (thinking about how we use it or where it can go)

Choose three of these ways of thinking that you remember using while working in this chapter. For each Way of Thinking that you choose, show and explain where you used it and how you used it. Describe why thinking in this way helped you solve a particular problem or understand something new. (For instance, explain why we wanted to **generalize** in this particular case, or why it was useful to see these particular connections.) Be sure to include examples to demonstrate your thinking.

Problem	Solution	Need Help?	More Practice
CL 9*1	$y > \frac{1}{2}x - 2$	MN p. 393	9*62, 9*63
CL 9*2	$y = -2x + 7$	MN p. 288, MN p. 314	9*44, 9*62, 9*76, 9*84, 9*87, 9*91, 9*103, 9*104, 9*107, 9*116
CL 9*3	Yes. The point (0, 4) lies on the graph $x^2 + 3x - 2 < y \le x - 3x + 4$. Therefore, it is a solution to the system of inequalities. 	9*36, 9*58	9*36, 9*54, 9*84
CL 9*4	a. $2x(x^2 + 4y)$ b. $(-3x + 2)(x - 7)$ c. not factorable d. $2(x + 3)(3x - 4)$	MN p. 337, 8*62	9*21, 9*23, 9*34, 9*40, 9*41, 9*66
CL 9*5	approximately 61.4 cups	MN p. 206	6*11, 6*58, 6*77, 7*7, 7*17, 7*42, 7*58, 7*67, 7*100

Problem	Solution	Need Help?	More Practice
CL 9*6	a. $x \geq 3$ b. $t < -\dfrac{7}{3}$ c. $y < 28$ d. $x > 2.5$	MN p. 375, MN p. 385	9*3, 9*8, 9*15, 9*18, 9*29, 9*64, 9*75, 9*83
CL 9*7	25 girls came to the dance.	MN p. 228, 6*3, 6*5	9*7, 9*16, 9*31
CL 9*8	a. $x = 1$ or $-\frac{7}{3}$ b. no solution	MN p. 347, MN p. 385, 8*94	9*9, 9*13, 9*14, 9*22, 9*45, 9*53, 9*85
CL 9*9	$x + 2 \leq y < x^2$	Lesson 9.3.1	9*59, 9*69, 9*74, 9*76, 9*84
CL 9*10	a. $y = -4x - 16$ b. $x = 10$ c. $y = 2x - 4$ d. $y = -\frac{1}{4}x + 2$	MN p. 295	9*19, 9*77, 9*81
CL 9*11	Audrey is less than 17 years old.	MN p. 375, MN p. 385	9*30, 9*52, 9*76, 9*82

Problem	Solution		Need Help?	More Practice
CL 9*12	a.	b.	MN p. 393	9*26, 9*27, 9*55, 9*63, 9*74
	c.			
CL 9*13	The tortoise catches up to the hare after 50 seconds.		MN p. 244	9*12, 9*33, 9*43, 9*56, 9*67, 9*86

CHAPTER 10   Simplifying and Solving

Since the beginning of this course, you have studied several different types of equations and have developed successful methods to solve them. For example, you have learned how to solve linear equations, systems of linear equations, and quadratic equations.

In Chapter 11, you will **extend** your solving skills to include other types of equations, including those with square roots, absolute values, and messy fractions.

Another focus of this chapter is learning how to simplify algebraic fractions (called rational expressions) and expressions with exponents. By using the special properties of the number 1 and the meaning of exponents, you will be able to simplify large, complicated expressions.

In this chapter, you will learn how to:

➢ Solve inequalities with absolute value.

➢ Simplify exponential expressions.

➢ Simplify rational expressions.

➢ Solve equations containing rational expressions.

➢ Solve quadratic equations by completing the square.

➢ Use multiple methods to solve new types of equations, including those with square roots and absolute values.

Guiding Questions

Think about these questions throughout this chapter:

How can I rewrite it?

How can I solve it?

Is there another method?

What is special about the number 1?

Chapter Outline

Section 10.1 In this section, you will study the properties of the number one and use them to simplify rational expressions. You will also use the meaning of an exponent to develop strategies to simplify exponential expressions. You will solve equations with fractions.

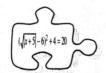

Section 10.2 In this section, you will develop new ways to solve unfamiliar, complicated equations involving square roots and absolute values.

Section 10.3 In this section, you will learn how to rewrite quadratics in perfect square form using a process called "completing the square."

10.1.1 How can I make it simpler?

Simplifying Expressions

Throughout this section you will learn new ways to simplify expressions. Later you will use your new skills to solve complex equations.

Today you will focus on a very special number (not zero this time, but very close): the number 1. What is special about 1? What can you do with the number 1 that you cannot do with any other number? You will use your understanding of the number 1 to simplify algebraic fractions.

10*1.   What do you know about the number 1? Brainstorm with your team and be ready to report to the class. Create examples to help show what you mean.

10*2.   Mr. Grek claims that anything divided by itself equals 1 (as long as you do not divide by zero!). For example, he says that $\frac{16x}{16x} = 1$ if x is not zero.

   a.   Is Mr. Grek correct?

   b.   Why can't x be zero?

   c.   Create your own rational expression (algebraic fraction) that equals 1. **Justify** that it equals one.

   d.   Mr. Grek also says that when you multiply any number by 1, the number stays the same. For example, he says that the product below equals $\frac{x}{y}$. Is he correct?

$$\boxed{1\tfrac{z}{z}} \cdot \frac{x}{y} = \frac{x}{y}$$

Note: For the rest of this chapter, we will assume that no denominator is equal to zero.

10*3.   Use what you know about the number 1 to simplify the expressions below, if possible. For each expression, assume the denominator is not zero.

   a. $\frac{x^2}{x^2}$

   b. $\frac{x}{x} \cdot \frac{x}{x} \cdot \frac{x}{3}$

   c. $\frac{x-2}{x-2} \cdot \frac{x+5}{x-1}$

   d. $\frac{9}{x} \cdot \frac{x}{9}$

   e. $\frac{h \cdot h \cdot k}{h}$

   f. $\frac{(2m-5)(m+6)}{(m+6)(3m+1)}$

   g. $\frac{6(n-2)}{3(n-2)}$

   h. $\frac{3-2x}{(4x-1)(3-2x)}$

10*4.   You have seen that we can rewrite expressions using the number one. We can also simplify using the meaning of an exponent.

An exponent is shorthand for repeated multiplication. For example, $n^4 = n \cdot n \cdot n \cdot n$.

a.   Expand each of the expressions below in the manner shown in the example.

i. y^7 ii. $5(2m)^3$ iii. $(x^3)^2$ iv. $4x^5 y^2$

b.   Simplify each of the expressions below using what you know about exponents and the number 1. Start by expanding the exponents, then simplify your results.

i. $\dfrac{x \cdot x \cdot x}{x}$ ii. $\dfrac{x^5}{x^2}$ iii. $x^2 \cdot x^3$ iv. $k^3 \cdot k^5$

v. $\dfrac{16k^3}{8k^2}$ vi. $m^6 \cdot m$ vii. $x^4 \cdot x^5 \cdot x^3$ viii. $\dfrac{6x^3 y}{2y}$

ix.   challenge: $\dfrac{5x^{50}}{10x^{15}}$

10*5.   Write a Learning Reflection about the number one. What is special about one? How can we use it to simplify expressions? Title this reflection "Simplifying with the Number One" and label it with today's date.

10*6.   Simplify these exponential expressions:

    a. $x^3 \cdot x^4$

    b. $\dfrac{2x^9}{x^6}$

    c. $(x^2)^3$

    d. $4xy^3 \cdot 7x^2y^3$

10*7.   Find a rule that represents the number of tiles in the tile pattern below.

    Figure 0   Figure 1   Figure 2

10*8.   A motion detector can record the distance between a moving person and the detector. Examine the graphs below, each generated when a different person walked in front of a motion detector. For each graph, describe the motion of the person: did they walk fast? slow? in what direction? If the motion is not possible, explain why.

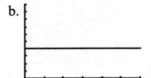 

10*9.   Solve the system of equations below using any method. Check your solution.

$$8y - 1 = x$$
$$10y - x = 5$$

10*10.   **Multiple Choice:** Which of the points below is a solution of $y < |x - 3|$?

    a.   (2, 1)   b.   (-4, 5)   c.   (-2, 8)   d.   (0, 3)

10*11.   Solve each of the following inequalities for the given variable. Represent your solutions on a number line.

    a. $5 + 3x < 5$

    b. $-3x \geq 8 - x$

10.1.2 How can I rewrite it?

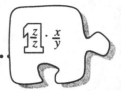

· ·

Simplifying Exponential Expressions

Today you will continue to simplify expressions with exponents using 1's and expansion. You will develop strategies to simplify expressions when the exponents are too large to expand on paper.

10*12.   Simplify each of the expressions below. Start by expanding the exponents and then simplify your results. Look for patterns or possible shortcuts that will help you to simplify more quickly. Be prepared to **justify** your patterns or shortcuts to the class.

a. $y^5 \cdot y^2$

b. $\frac{w^5}{w^2}$

c. $(x^2)^4$

d. $x^{10} \cdot x^{12}$

e. $\frac{13p^4q^5}{p^2q^2}$

f. $(\frac{x^2}{y})^3$

g. $5h \cdot 2h^{24}$

h. $\frac{10m^{30}}{2m^8}$

i. $(3k^{20})^4$

j. $\frac{24hg^2}{3hg^9}$

k. $(\frac{m^3}{n^{10}})^4$

l. $w^4 \cdot p \cdot w^3$

10*13.   George is simplifying expressions with very large exponents. He arrives at each of the results below. For each result, decide if he is correct and **justify** your answer using the meaning of exponents.

a. $\frac{x^{150}}{x^{50}} = x^3$

b. $y^{20} \cdot y^{41} = y^{61}$

c. $(8m^2n^{15})^3 = 8m^6n^{45}$

10*14.   Lacey and Haley are simplifying expressions.

a.   Haley simplifies $x^3 \cdot x^2$ and **gets** x^5. Lacey simplifies
$x^3 + x^2$ and gets the same result! Who is correct? Show
how you know. Explain the mistake that one of the girls
made.

b.   Haley simplifies $3^5 \cdot 4^5$ and gets the result 12^{10}, but Lacey is not sure. Is Haley
correct? Be sure to **justify** your answer.

10*15.   Work with your team to write four exponent problems that each has a solution of x^{12}.
At least one problem must involve multiplication, one must involve grouping, and one
must involve division. Be creative!

10*16.   EXPONENT CONCENTRATION: A GAME

Split your team into two pairs and decide which is Pair One and which is Pair Two.
Your teacher will distribute a set of cards for a game called Exponent Concentration.
The game is described below.

- Arrange the cards face down into a rectangular grid.

- Pair One selects and turns over two cards.

- If Pair One thinks the values on the cards are equivalent, they must **justify** this
claim to Pair Two. Once everyone in the team agrees, Pair One takes the pair.
This is the end of their turn.

- If the values are not equivalent, Pair One returns both cards to their original face
down position. This is the end of their turn.

- Pair Two repeats the process.

- Pairs alternate until no cards remain face down. The pair with the most matches
wins.

10*17. Use what you have learned about exponents to rewrite each of the expressions below.

    a. $\dfrac{h^9}{h^{11}}$
            b. $(3k^5)^2$
            c. $\dfrac{16x^4y^3}{2x^4}$

10*18. Write the inequality represented by the graph at right.

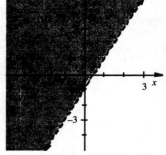

10*19. Chad is entering a rocket competition. He needs to program his rocket so that when it is launched from the ground it lands 20 feet away. In order to qualify, it must be 100 feet off the ground at its highest point. What equation should he program into his rocket launcher to win? Let x represent the distance from the launch pad in feet and y represent the height of the rocket in feet. Draw a sketch of the rocket's path.

10*20. How many solutions does each quadratic equation below have?

    a. $6x^2 + 7x - 20 = 0$
            b. $m^2 - 8m + 16 = 0$

    c. $2r^2 + r + 3 = 0$
            d. $(2k + 1)^2 = 0$

10*21. A piece of metal at 20°C is warmed at a steady rate of 2 degrees every minute. At the same time, another piece of metal at 240°C is cooled at a steady rate of 3 degrees every minute. After how many minutes is the temperature of each piece of metal the same? Explain how you found your answer.

10*22. **Multiple Choice:** $x = 2$ is a solution for which of the equations or inequalities below?

    a. $\frac{x-4}{3} = \frac{x}{15}$
    b. $(x-2)^2 < 0$
    c. $|3x - 8| \geq -1$
    d. $\sqrt{x + 2} = 16$

10.1.3 How can I rewrite it?

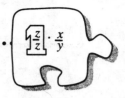

Zero and Negative Exponents and Scientific Notation

Today you will use the patterns you found in Lesson 10.1.2 to figure out the meaning of zero and negative exponents. Then you will use positive and negative exponents to express very large and very small numbers in scientific notation.

10*23. George wants to **generalize** the patterns for working with exponents. With your study team, summarize the patterns you found in Lesson 10.1.2. Describe how to write the expressions below as simply as possible. For each description, include the words **base** and **exponent**.

    a. $x^{25} \cdot x^{40} = ?$ **generalization:** $x^n \cdot x^m = ?$ What patterns did you find?

    b. $\frac{x^{36}}{x^{13}} = ?$ **generalization:** $\frac{x^n}{x^m} = ?$ What patterns did you find?

    c. $(x^5)^{12} = ?$ **generalization:** $(x^n)^m = ?$ What patterns did you find?

10*24. Use the patterns you described in problem 10*23 to rewrite each expression below as simply as possible.

    a. $x^7 \cdot x^4$ b. $(x^3)^3$ c. $x^6 \div x^2$ d. $\frac{m}{m^8}$

    e. $(2x^2)^4$ f. $(x^2y^2)^4$ g. $\frac{x^2y^{11}}{x^5y^3}$ h. $\frac{2x^{12}}{3x^2}$

10*25. Describe everything you know about $\frac{x^m}{x^m}$. What is its value? How can you rewrite it using a single exponent? What new conclusions can you draw? Be prepared to explain your findings to the class.

10*26. Problem 10*25 helped us recognize that $x^0 = 1$. We will similarly use division to explore the meaning of x^{-1}, x^{-2}, etc. Simplify each of the expressions below twice:

- once by expanding the terms and simplifying, and

- again by using your new pattern for division with exponents.

Be ready to discuss the meaning of negative exponents with the class.

    a. $\frac{x^4}{x^5}$ b. $\frac{x^2}{x^4}$ c. $\frac{x^7}{x^{10}}$

10*27. Use your exponent patterns to rewrite each of the expressions below. For example, if the original expression has a negative exponent, then rewrite the expression so that it has no negative exponents and vice versa. Also, if the expression contains multiplication or division, then use your exponent rules to simplify the expression.

a. k^{-5} b. m^0 c. $x^{-2} \cdot x^5$ d. $\frac{1}{p^2}$

e. $\frac{y^{-2}}{y^{-3}}$ f. $(x^{-2})^3$ g. $(a^2b)^{-1}$ h. $\frac{1}{x^{-1}}$

10*28. Another use of exponents is to help us represent very large (and very small) numbers. For example, a very large number like the one below can be difficult to write out in complete form (called **standard form**).

$$3,000,000,000,000,000,000,000,000,000,000$$

Instead, we can write this number using **scientific notation** as $3 \cdot 10^{30}$. This short hand notation is not only easier to write and easier to enter into our calculators, but it also gives us an immediate sense of how large the number is. Since 10^{30} is 10 multiplied by itself thirty times, then we know that $3 \cdot 10^{30}$ is the number 3 with 30 zeros after it.

Likewise, $1.4 \cdot 10^8$ is 1.4 multiplied by 10 eight times. Thus $1.4 \cdot 10^8 = 140,000,000$. Scientific notation is also useful for writing small numbers, like 0.00024. Since $0.00024 = \frac{24}{100000}$, we can rewrite the number using scientific notation as $2.4 \cdot 10^{-4}$.

a. Scientists claim that the earth is about $4.6 \cdot 10^9$ years old. Write this number in standard form.

b. The average distance between the earth and the sun is about 150,000,000,000 meters. Translate this number into scientific notation.

c. It takes light about $3.3 \cdot 10^{-9}$ seconds to travel 1 meter. Express this number in standard form.

10*29. Scientific notation is not only a convenient way to write very large and very small numbers, but it also makes them easier to put into our calculators.

    a. For example, multiply $5,000 \cdot 20,000,000,000,000$ and express the answer in standard form. If these numbers cannot be entered into your calculator, then multiply them by hand on your paper.

    b. Now multiply these same numbers by first changing each into scientific notation. For example, $5000 = 5 \cdot 10^3$. Express your answer in scientific notation.

    c. Which method was easier and why?

10*30. In a Learning Reflection, describe the meaning of zero and negative exponents. That is, explain how to interpret x^0 and x^{-1}. Title this reflection "Zero and Negative Exponents" and include today's date.

LOOKING DEEPER

Inductive and Deductive Reasoning

MATH NOTES

When you make a conclusion based on a pattern, you are using **Inductive Reasoning.** So far in this course you have used inductive reasoning repeatedly to **generalize** patterns. For example, in Lessons 10.1.1 through 10.1.3, you used patterns to generalize the fact that $x^n x^m = x^{n+m}$ and that $(x^n)^m = x^{nm}$.

However, conclusions can also be reached using logic based on facts. This is called **Deductive Reasoning**. You used deductive reasoning during this lesson when you determined that $x^{-1} = \frac{1}{x}$. See the logical deduction below.

Statement	Reason
Since $\frac{x^4}{x^5} = x^{-1}$	This is true because $\frac{x^m}{x^n} = x^{m-n}$.
And since $\frac{x^4}{x^5} = \frac{x \cdot x \cdot x \cdot x}{x \cdot x \cdot x \cdot x \cdot x} = \frac{1}{x}$	This is true because $\frac{x}{x} = 1$.
Therefore, $x^{-1} = \frac{1}{x}$.	This is true because $\frac{x^4}{x^5}$ equals both x^{-1} and $\frac{1}{x}$, so $x^{-1} = \frac{1}{x}$. (This is called the Transitive Property of Equality.)

10*31.   Simplify each of the expressions below. Your final simplification should contain no negative exponents.

   a. $(5x^3)(-3x^{-2})$ b. $(4p^2q)^3$ c. $\frac{3m^7}{m^{-1}}$

10*32.   Neil A. Armstrong was the first person ever to walk on the moon. After his historic landing on July 20, 1969, he stepped onto the Moon's surface and spoke the famous phrase, "That's one small step for a man, one giant leap for mankind."

His craft, Apollo 11, traveled 238,900 miles from the Earth to reach the moon. How many feet was this?
Express your answer in both standard form and in scientific notation. Round your decimal to the nearest hundredth. (Note: There are 5,280 feet in each mile.)

10*33.   How many solutions do each of the equations below have?

   a. $4x + 3 = 3x + 3$ b. $3(x - 4) - x = 5 + 2x$

   c. $(5x - 2)(x + 4) = 0$ d. $x^2 - 4x + 4 = 0$

10*34.   While David was solving the equation $100x + 300 = 500$, he wondered if he could first change the equation to $x + 3 = 5$. What do you think?

   a.   Solve both equations and verify that they have the same solution.

   b.   What could you do to the equation $100x + 300 = 500$ to change it into $x + 3 = 5$?

10*35.   Solve the system of equations below by <u>graphing</u>. Write your solution(s) in (x, y) form.

$$y = -4x - 2$$
$$y = x^2 - 3x - 4$$

10.1.4   How can I rewrite it?

Fractional Exponents and Rational Expressions

So far you have discovered ways to deal with exponents when multiplying and dividing. You have also found ways to interpret expressions when the exponent is zero or negative. But what if the exponent is a fraction? And how can exponents help us rewrite numbers? Today you will develop an understanding for fractional exponents and learn about scientific notation, a way to use exponents to write very large or very small numbers.

10*36.   **FRACTIONAL EXPONENTS**

What happens when an exponent is a fraction? Consider this as you answer the questions below.

a.   Calculate $9^{1/2}$ with your scientific calculator. What is the result? Also use your calculator to find $49^{1/2}$ and $100^{1/2}$. What effect does having $\frac{1}{2}$ in the exponent appear to have?

b.   Based on your observation in part (a), predict the value of $4^{\frac{1}{2}}$ and $(7^{\frac{1}{2}})^2$. Then, confirm your prediction with your calculator.

c.   What about other fractional exponents? What effect does raising a number to the $\frac{1}{3}$ power have? Use your calculator to find $8^{\frac{1}{3}}$, $27^{\frac{1}{3}}$ and $64^{\frac{1}{3}}$ to test your theory.

d.   Was the reasoning you used in parts (a) and (c) an example of inductive or deductive reasoning? Refer to the Math Notes box at the end of Lesson 10.1.3 to help you decide.

Square Root: $x^{\frac{1}{2}} = \sqrt{x}$ **Cube Root:** $x^{\frac{1}{3}} = \sqrt[3]{x}$

10*37.   Now that you have many tools to rewrite expressions with exponents, use these tools together to rewrite each of the expressions below. For example, $\sqrt{2^5} = (2^5)^{1/2} = 2^{5/2}$ since square rooting is the same as raising a number to the one-half power.

a. $(\sqrt{3})^4$ b. $10^{\frac{7}{2}}$ c. $\sqrt[3]{2^5}$

10*38. Match each expression below on the left (letters a through h) with an equivalent expression on the right (#1 – 8). Assume $x > 0$.

a. $\sqrt{x^3}$ e. $\sqrt[3]{x^2}$ ‖ 1. x^{-2} 5. $\sqrt{x}$

b. x^{-3} f. 1 2. x 6. $x^{\frac{2}{3}}$

c. $(\sqrt[3]{x})^5$ g. $x^{-3}x^4$ 3. $x^{\frac{3}{2}}$ 7. $x^{\frac{5}{3}}$

d. $\frac{1}{x^2}$ h. $(x^{\frac{1}{4}})^2$ 4. x^0 8. $\frac{x^2}{x^5}$

10*39. Mr. Grek tries to simplify $\frac{4x}{x}$ and $\frac{4+x}{x}$.

a. Mr. Grek thinks that since $\frac{x}{x} = 1$, then $\frac{4x}{x} = 4$. Is he correct? Substitute three values of x to **justify** your answer.

b. He thinks that because $\frac{x}{x} = 1$, then $\frac{4+x}{x} = 5$. Is he correct? Substitute three values of x to **justify** your answer.

c. Compare these two results. When can a rational expression be simplified in this manner?

d. Which of the following expressions below is simplified correctly?

i. $\frac{x^2 + x + 3}{x+3} = x^2$ ii. $\frac{(x+2)(x+3)}{x+3} = x+2$

10*40. Factor the numerator and denominator of each fraction, if necessary. Then look for "ones" and simplify. For each expression, assume the denominator is not zero.

a. $\frac{x^2 + 6x + 9}{x^2 - 9}$ b. $\frac{2x^2 - x - 10}{3x^2 + 7x + 2}$

c. $\frac{28x^2 - x - 15}{28x^2 - x - 15}$ d. $\frac{x^2 + 4x}{2x + 8}$

10*41. Write a Learning Reflection explaining how to simplify rational expressions such as those in problem 10*40. Be sure to include an example. Title this reflection "Simplifying Rational Expressions" and include today's date.

LOOKING DEEPER

Summary of the Rules of Exponents

MATH NOTES

Terms: In the expression x^3, x is the **base** and 3 is the **exponent**.

$$x^3 = x \cdot x \cdot x$$

The patterns that you have been using during this section of the book are called the **Laws of Exponents**. Here are the basic rules with examples:

a. $x^m x^n = x^{m+n}$ examples: $x^3 x^4 = x^{3+4} = x^7$; $2^5 \cdot 2^{-1} = 2^4$

b. $\dfrac{x^m}{x^n} = x^{m-n}$ if $x \neq 0$ examples: $x^{10} \div x^4 = x^{10-4} = x^6$; $\dfrac{5^4}{5^7} = 5^{-3}$

c. $(x^m)^n = x^{mn}$ examples: $(x^4)^3 = x^{4 \cdot 3} = x^{12}$; $(10^5)^6 = 10^{30}$

d. $x^0 = 1$ if $x \neq 0$ examples: $\dfrac{y^2}{y^2} = y^0 = 1$; $9^0 = 1$

e. $x^{-1} = \frac{1}{x}$, if $x \neq 0$ examples: $\dfrac{1}{x^2} = (\frac{1}{x})^2 = (x^{-1})^2 = x^{-2}$; $3^{-1} = \frac{1}{3}$

f. $x^{1/m} = \sqrt[m]{x}$, if $x \geq 0$ examples: $\sqrt{k} = k^{1/2}$; $y^{2/3} = \sqrt[3]{y^2}$

10*42. If necessary, rewrite the numerator and denominator of each rational expression as a product. Then look for "ones" and simplify. Assume that the denominators do not equal zero.

a. $\dfrac{(x+4)^2}{(x+4)(x-2)}$

b. $\dfrac{8(x+2)^3(x-3)^3}{4(x+2)^2(x-3)^5}$

c. $\dfrac{x^2+3x}{x^2+6x+9}$

d. $\dfrac{2x^2+6x+4}{4x^2-12x-16}$

10*43. Lesson 10.1.5 will focus on multiplying and dividing rational expressions. Review what you learned about multiplying and dividing fractions in a previous course as you answer the questions below. For your assistance, the following examples have been provided.

$$\tfrac{9}{16} \cdot \tfrac{4}{6} = \tfrac{36}{96} = \tfrac{3}{8}$$

$$\tfrac{5}{6} \div \tfrac{20}{12} = \tfrac{5}{6} \cdot \tfrac{12}{20} = \tfrac{60}{120} = \tfrac{1}{2}$$

a. Without a calculator, multiply $\tfrac{2}{3} \cdot \tfrac{9}{14}$ and reduce the result. Then use a calculator to check your answer. Describe your method for multiplying fractions.

b. Without a calculator, divide $\tfrac{3}{5} \div \tfrac{12}{25}$ and reduce the result. Then use a calculator to check your answer. Describe your method for dividing fractions.

10*44. Solve the equations below. Check your solution(s).

a. $\tfrac{m}{6} = \tfrac{m+1}{5}$

b. $\tfrac{3x-5}{2} = \tfrac{4x+1}{4}$

c. $\tfrac{8}{k} = \tfrac{14}{k+3}$

d. $\tfrac{x}{9} = 10$

10*45. Using your knowledge of exponents, rewrite each expression below so that there are no negative exponents or parentheses remaining.

a. $\dfrac{4x^{18}}{2x^{22}}$

b. $(s^4tu^2)(s^7t^{-1})$

c. $(3w^{-2})^4$

d. m^{-3}

10*46. Jessica has 3 more candies than twice the number Sean has. If Sean has s candies, write an expression to represent how many candies Jessica has.

10.1.5 How can I multiply it?

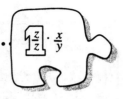

Multiplying and Dividing Rational Expressions

In a previous course you learned how to multiply and divide fractions. But what if the fractions are rational expressions? Is the process the same? Today you will learn how to multiply and divide rational expressions and will continue to practice simplifying rational expressions.

10*47. Review what you learned yesterday as you simplify the rational expression below. What are the excluded values of x? (That is, what values can x <u>not</u> be?)

$$\frac{3x^2+11x-4}{2x^2+11x+12}$$

10*48. With your team, review your responses to homework problem 10*43. Verify that everyone obtained the same answers and be prepared to share with the class how you multiplied and divided fractions.

$$\frac{2}{3} \cdot \frac{9}{14} \qquad\qquad \frac{3}{5} \div \frac{12}{25}$$

10*49. Use your understanding of multiplying and dividing fractions to rewrite the expressions below. Then look for "ones" and simplify. For each rational expression, assume the denominator is not zero.

a. $\dfrac{4x+3}{x-5} \cdot \dfrac{x-5}{x+3}$

b. $\dfrac{x+2}{9x-1} \div \dfrac{2x+1}{9x-1}$

c. $\dfrac{2m+3}{3m-2} \cdot \dfrac{7+4m}{3+2m}$

d. $\dfrac{(y-2)^2}{3y} \cdot \dfrac{y+5}{(y+2)(y-2)}$

e. $\dfrac{15x^3}{3xy} \div \dfrac{10x^2y}{4y^2}$

f. $\dfrac{(5x-2)(3x+1)}{(2x-3)^2} \div \dfrac{(5x-2)(x-4)}{(x-4)(2x-3)}$

10*50. PUTTING IT ALL TOGETHER

Multiply or divide the expressions below. Leave your answer as simplified as possible. For each rational expression, assume the denominator is not zero.

a. $\dfrac{20}{22} \cdot \dfrac{14}{35}$

b. $\dfrac{12}{40} \div \dfrac{15}{6}$

c. $\dfrac{5x-15}{3x^2+10x-8} \div \dfrac{x^2+x-12}{3x^2-8x+4}$

d. $\dfrac{12x-18}{x^2-2x-15} \cdot \dfrac{x^2-x-12}{3x^2-9x-12}$

e. $\dfrac{5x^2+34x-7}{10x} \cdot \dfrac{5x}{x^2+4x-21}$

f. $\dfrac{2x^2+x-10}{x^2+2x-8} \div \dfrac{4x^2+20x+25}{x+4}$

10*51. In a Learning Reflection, explain how to multiply and divide rational expressions. Be sure to include an example of each. Title this reflection "Multiplying and Dividing Rational Expressions" and include today's date.

METHODS AND MEANINGS

Simplifying Rational Expressions

To simplify a rational expression, both the numerator and denominator must be written as a product. Then look for factors that make ONE (1) and simplify. Study the examples below.

Example 1: $\dfrac{x^2+5x+4}{x^2+x-12} = \dfrac{(x+4)(x+1)}{(x+4)(x-3)} = 1 \cdot \dfrac{x+1}{x-3} = \dfrac{x+1}{x-3}$ *for $x \neq -4$ or 3*

Example 2: $\dfrac{2x-7}{2x^2+3x-35} = \dfrac{(2x-7)(1)}{(2x-7)(x+5)} = 1 \cdot \dfrac{1}{x+5} = \dfrac{1}{x+5}$ *for $x \neq -5$ or $\frac{7}{2}$*

Review & Preview

10*52. Graph the system of inequalities below on graph paper. Shade the region that represents the solution.

$$y \geq x^2 - 4$$
$$y \leq -x^2 + 4$$

10*53. Rewrite each expression below so that there are no negative exponents or parentheses remaining.

a. $\dfrac{8a^{11}}{4a^{20}}$

b. $(p^3q)(p^4q^{-1}t)$

c. $(9m^{-3})^2$

d. h^0

e. $x^2(2x^3 - 5)$

f. $(x^4)^3 \cdot (x^{-3})^2$

g. $\dfrac{(5x^2y^3)^2}{15x^2y^{-3}}$

h. w^{-2}

10*54. Multiply or divide the expressions below. Leave your answer as simplified as possible. For each expression, assume the denominator is not zero.

a. $\frac{(3x-1)(x+7)}{4(2x-5)} \cdot \frac{10(2x-5)}{(4x+1)(x+7)}$

b. $\frac{(m-3)(m+11)}{(2m+5)(m-3)} \div \frac{(4m-3)(m+11)}{(4m-3)(2m+5)}$

c. $\frac{2p^2+5p-12}{2p^2-5p+3} \cdot \frac{p^2+8p-9}{3p^2+10p-8}$

d. $\frac{4x-12}{x^2+3x-10} \div \frac{2x^2-13x+21}{2x^2+3x-35}$

10*55. Now David wants to solve the equation $4000x - 8000 = 16000$.

a. What _easier_ equation could he solve instead that would give him the same solution? (In other words, what equivalent equation has easier numbers to work with?)

b. **Justify** that your equation in part (a) is equivalent to $4000x - 8000 = 16000$ by showing that they have the same solution.

c. David's last equation to solve is $\frac{x}{100} + \frac{3}{100} = \frac{8}{100}$. Write and solve an equivalent equation with friendly numbers that would give him the same answer.

10*56. Find the slope and y-intercept of each line below.

a. $y = \frac{-6}{5}x - 7$

b. $3x - 2y = 10$

c. The line through the points (5, -2) and (8, 4).

10*57. Solve the systems of equations below using any method.

a. $3x - 3 = y$
$6x - 5y = 12$

b. $3x - 2y = 30$
$2x + 3y = -19$

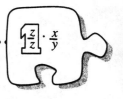
Fraction Busters

The past two lessons have focused on how to multiply, divide, and simplify rational expressions. How can we use these skills to help solve problems?

10*58.   Review what you learned in Lesson 10.1.5 by multiplying or dividing the expressions below. Simplify your result. For each rational expression, assume the denominator is not zero.

   a. $\frac{x-7}{9(2x-1)} \div \frac{(x+5)(x-7)}{6x(x+5)}$

   b. $\frac{6x^2-x-1}{3x^2+25x+8} \cdot \frac{x^2+4x-32}{2x^2+7x-4}$

10*59.   Cassie wants to solve the quadratic equation $x^2 + 1.5x - 2.5 = 0$. "I think I need to use the Quadratic Formula because of the decimals," she told Claudia. Suddenly, Claudia blurted out, "No, Cassie! I think there is another way. Can't you first rewrite this equation so it has no decimals?"

   a.   What is Claudia talking about? Explain what she means. Then rewrite the equation so that it has no decimals.

   b.   Now solve the new equation (the one without decimals). Check your solution(s).

10*60.   SOLVING BY REWRITING

   Rewriting $x^2 + 1.5x - 2.5 = 0$ in problem 10*59 gave us a new, **equivalent** equation that was much easier to solve. If needed, refer to the Math Notes box for this lesson for more information about equivalent equations.

   How can each equation below be rewritten so that it is easier to solve? With your team, find an equivalent equation for each one that has no fractions or decimals and that has numbers that are reasonably small. Strive to find the *simplest* equation. Then solve the new equation and check your answer(s).

   a. $32(3x) - 32(5) = 32(7)$

   b. $9000x^2 - 6000x - 15000 = 0$

   c. $\frac{1}{3} + \frac{x}{3} = \frac{10}{3}$

   d. $2x^2 + 4x - 2.5 = 0$

10*61.   Examine the equation below.

$$\tfrac{x}{6} - \tfrac{5}{8} = 4$$

   a.   Multiply each term by 6. What happened? Do any fractions remain?

   b.   If you have not already done so, decide how you can change your result from part (a) so that no fractions remain. Then solve the resulting equation.

   c.   Multiplying $\tfrac{x}{6} - \tfrac{5}{8} = 4$ by six did not eliminate all the fractions. What could we have multiplied $\tfrac{x}{6} - \tfrac{5}{8} = 4$ by to get rid of all the fractions? Explain how you got your answer and write the equivalent equation that has no fractions.

   d.   Solve the equation and check your solution in the original equation.

10*62.   Now you are going to **reverse** the process. Your teacher will give your team a simple equation that you need to "complicate." That is, change the equation to make it seem harder (although you know it is still equivalent to the easy equation).

   a.   Verify that your new equation is equivalent to the one assigned by your teacher.

   b.   Share your new equation with the class by posting it on the overhead projector or chalkboard.

   c.   Copy down the equations generated by your class on another piece of paper. You will need these equations for problem 10*64 in the homework.

METHODS AND MEANINGS

Equivalent Equations

MATH NOTES

Two equations are **equivalent** if they have all the same solutions. There are many ways to change one equation into a different, equivalent equation. Common ways include: *adding* the same number to both sides, *subtracting* the same number from both sides, *multiplying* both sides by the same number, *dividing* both sides by the same (non-zero) number, and *rewriting* one or both sides of the equation.

These equations are all equivalent: $2x + 1 = 3$ $20x + 10 = 30$

$2(x + 0.5) = 3$ $\tfrac{2x}{3} + \tfrac{1}{3} = 1$ $0.002x + 0.001 = 0.003$

METHODS AND MEANINGS

Multiplying and Dividing Rational Expressions

Just as we can multiply and divide fractions, we can multiply and divide rational expressions.

Problem A: Multiply $\dfrac{x^2 + 6x}{(x+6)^2} \cdot \dfrac{x^2 + 7x + 6}{x^2 - 1}$ and simplify your result.

After factoring, our expression becomes: $\dfrac{x(x+6)}{(x+6)(x+6)} \cdot \dfrac{(x+6)(x+1)}{(x+1)(x-1)}$

After multiplying, reorder the factors: $\dfrac{(x+6)}{(x+6)} \cdot \dfrac{(x+6)}{(x+6)} \cdot \dfrac{x}{(x-1)} \cdot \dfrac{(x+1)}{(x+1)}$

Since $\dfrac{(x+6)}{(x+6)} = 1$ and $\dfrac{(x+1)}{(x+1)} = 1$, simplify: $1 \cdot 1 \cdot \dfrac{x}{x-1} \cdot 1 \Rightarrow \dfrac{x}{x-1}$.

Problem B: Divide $\dfrac{x^2 - 4x - 5}{x^2 - 4x + 4} \div \dfrac{x^2 - 2x - 15}{x^2 + 4x - 12}$ and simplify your result.

First, change to a multiplication expression: $\dfrac{x^2 - 4x - 5}{x^2 - 4x + 4} \cdot \dfrac{x^2 + 4x - 12}{x^2 - 2x - 15}$

After factoring, we get: $\dfrac{(x-5)(x+1)}{(x-2)(x-2)} \cdot \dfrac{(x+6)(x-2)}{(x-5)(x+3)}$

After multiplying, reorder the factors: $\dfrac{(x-5)}{(x-5)} \cdot \dfrac{(x-2)}{(x-2)} \cdot \dfrac{(x+1)}{(x-2)} \cdot \dfrac{(x+6)}{(x+3)}$

Since $\dfrac{(x-5)}{(x-5)} = 1$ and $\dfrac{(x-2)}{(x-2)} = 1$, simplify: $\dfrac{(x+1)(x+6)}{(x-2)(x+3)}$

Thus, $\dfrac{x^2 - 4x - 5}{x^2 - 4x + 4} \div \dfrac{x^2 - 2x - 15}{x^2 + 4x - 12} = \dfrac{(x+1)(x+6)}{(x-2)(x+3)}$ or $\dfrac{x^2 + 7x + 6}{x^2 + x - 6}$

All of these steps assume that the denominators are not equal to zero. So in Problem A, $x \neq -6, 1, or -1$; in Problem B, $x \neq 2, 5, or -3$.

10*63.   Rewrite each of the expressions below. For example, if the expression has a negative exponent, then rewrite the expression so it has no negative exponents. If the expression contains multiplication or division, then use your exponent rules to simplify the expression.

a. y^0

b. $27x^2y \div 6x^3$

c. $\frac{(x-3)^9}{(x-3)^5}$ *for x ≠ 3*

d. $(5p^{-2}q)(6p^2q^5)$

e. $(5m^3)^2(2m^2)^3$

f. $\frac{(2x^3)^2}{2x^4}$ *for x ≠ 0*

10*64.   Solve the equations generated by your class in problem 10*62. Be sure to check each solution and show all work.

10*65.   Simplify the rational expressions below.

a. $\frac{x^2-8x+16}{3x^2-10x-8}$ *for x ≠ $-\frac{2}{3}$ or 4*

b. $\frac{10x+25}{2x^2-x-15}$ *for x ≠ $-\frac{5}{2}$ or 3*

c. $\frac{9x^4y^3z}{3x^4y^3z}$ *for x, y, and z ≠ 0*

10*66.   Find the equation of the line parallel to $y = -\frac{1}{3}x + 5$ through the point (9, -1).

10*67.   Write the inequality for the graph at right.

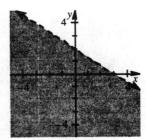

10*68.   Write and solve an inequality to represent the situation below. Write your solution as a sentence.

Vinita wants to rent a skateboard and only has $20. She found out that the shop will charge her $8 to rent the skateboard plus $3.75 per hour. She does not know how long she wants to rent it. What are her options?

10.1.7 How can I solve it?

More Fraction Busters

In Lesson 10.1.6, you learned a powerful new method to help solve complicated equations: rewriting the equation first to create a simpler, equivalent equation. Today you will continue to solve new, complicated equations and will focus specifically on equations with fractions. As you solve these new problems, look for ways to **connect** today's work with what you have learned previously.

10*69.   Examine the equation below.

$$\frac{5x}{3} + \frac{15}{2} = \frac{5}{2}$$

    a.   Solve the equation by first finding an equivalent equation without fractions. Check your solution(s).

    b.   Often this method of eliminating fractions from an equation is called the **Fraction Busters Method** because the multiplication of the equation by a common denominator or several of the denominators eliminates ("busts") the fractions. The result is an equation with only integers.

        What number (or numbers) did you multiply both sides of the equation by to eliminate the fractions? How did you choose that number? Is it the smallest number that would eliminate all the fractions?

10*70.   Work with your team to solve each of the equations below by first finding an equivalent equation that contains no fractions. Each problem presents new challenges and situations. Be ready to share how you solved each problem and why you did what you did with the class. Remember to check each solution.

    a. $\frac{x}{4} - \frac{x}{6} = \frac{2}{3}$

    b. $\frac{5}{x} - 2x = 3$ *for* $x \neq 0$

    c. $\frac{-2x+1}{3} - \frac{x+3}{7} = 8$

    d. $\frac{x+3}{x-2} + 2 = \frac{x+5}{x-2}$ *for* $x \neq 2$

10*71.   Now examine the equation below.

$$\frac{4+p}{p^2+2p-8} + 3 = \frac{4}{p-2}$$

a.   What values of p are not allowed?

b.   Use your new skills to rewrite the equation below so that it has no fractions. Then solve the new equation. Check your solution(s). What happened?

10*72.   Solve the equations below by first changing each equation to a simpler, equivalent equation. Check your solution(s).

a. $50x^2 + 200x = -150$

b. $\frac{a}{9} + \frac{1}{a} = \frac{2}{3}$ for $a \neq 0$

c. $1.2m - 0.2 = 3.8 + m$

d. $\frac{2}{x+5} + \frac{3x}{x^2+2x-15} = \frac{4}{x-3}$ for $x \neq -5$ or 3

METHODS AND MEANINGS

Solving Equations with Algebraic Fractions
Fraction Busters

Solve: $\frac{x}{3} + \frac{x}{5} = 2$

The complicating issue in this problem is dealing with the fractions. We could add them by first writing them in terms of a common denominator, but there is an easier way.

There is no need to use the often time consuming process of adding the fractions if we can "eliminate" the denominators. To do this, we will need to find a common denominator of all fractions, and then we will multiply both sides of the equation by that common denominator. In this case the lowest common denominator is 15, so we multiply both sides of the equation by 15.

The result is an equivalent equation without fractions!

The number we use to eliminate the denominators is called a **FRACTION BUSTER**. Now the equation looks like many we have seen before and we solve it in the usual way.

Finally, remember to check your answer.

$\frac{x}{3} + \frac{x}{5} = 2$

The lowest common denominator of $\frac{x}{3}$ and $\frac{x}{5}$ is 15.

$$15 \cdot \left(\frac{x}{3} + \frac{x}{5}\right) = 15 \cdot 2$$

$$15 \cdot \frac{x}{3} + 15 \cdot \frac{x}{5} = 15 \cdot 2$$

$$5x + 3x = 30$$

$$8x = 30$$

$$x = \frac{30}{8} = \frac{15}{4} = 3.75$$

$$\frac{3.75}{3} + \frac{3.75}{5} = 2$$

$$1.25 + 0.75 = 2$$

Simplifying and Solving

431

10*73. Solve the equations below by first changing each equation to a simpler equivalent equation. Check your solution(s).

a. $3000x - 2000 = 10000$

b. $\frac{x^2}{2} + \frac{3x}{2} - 5 = 0$

c. $\frac{5}{2}x - \frac{1}{3} = 13$

d. $\frac{3}{10} + \frac{2x}{5} = \frac{1}{2}$

10*74. Multiply or divide the expressions below. Express your answers as simply as possible. Assume the denominators do not equal zero.

a. $\frac{5x^2 - 11x + 2}{x^2 + 8x + 16} \cdot \frac{x^2 + 10x + 24}{10x^2 + 13x - 3}$

b. $\frac{6x + 3}{2x - 3} \div \frac{3x^2 - 12x - 15}{2x^2 - x - 3}$

10*75. In order to miss a sand trap, a golfer hits a ball so that its height is represented by the equation $h = -16t^2 + 80t$, where h is the height measured in feet and t is the time measured in seconds.

a. When does the ball land on the ground?

b. How high does the ball travel?

10*76. Write and solve an equation (or a system of equations) for the following situation. Be sure to define your variables.

Each morning, Jerry delivers two different newspapers: the Tribune and the Star. The Times weighs $\frac{1}{2}$ a pound and the Star weighs $\frac{1}{4}$ a pound. If he delivers a total of 27 newspapers that weigh a total of $11\frac{1}{2}$ pounds, how many Tribunes does he deliver?

10*77. Solve the equations and inequalities below. If necessary, write your solution in approximate form.

a. $900x - 200 = 500x + 600$

b. $3k^2 - 15k + 14 = 0$

c. $|x - 4| < 6$

d. $\frac{7}{3} + \frac{x}{2} = \frac{6x - 1}{6}$

10*78. Graph the inequality $y > |x - 2| + 1$ on graph paper.

Algebra Connections: Chapter 10

10.2.1 How can I solve it?

Multiple Methods for Solving Equations

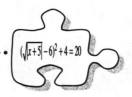

So far in this course you have developed many different methods for solving equations, such as adding things to both sides of the equation or multiplying each term by a number to eliminate fractions. But how would you solve a complicated equation such as $(\sqrt{|x+5|}-6)^2+4=20$?

By looking at equations in different ways you will be able to solve some equations much more quickly and easily. These new approaches will also allow you to solve new kinds of equations you have not studied before. As you solve equations in today's lesson, ask yourself these questions:

How can I see it?

Is there another way?

10*79. DIFFERENT METHODS TO SOLVE AN EQUATION

By the end this section you will be able to solve the equation $(\sqrt{|x+5|}-6)^2+4=20$. This equation is very complex and will require you to look at solving equations in new ways. In order to be prepared for other strange and unfamiliar equations, we will first examine all the solving tools we currently have by solving a comparatively easier equation:

$$4(x+3)=20$$

Your Task: With your team, find the value of x in the equation above in **at least** two different ways. Explain how you found x in each case and be prepared to share your explanations with the class.

Further Guidance

10*80. SOLVING BY REWRITING

David wants to find x in the equation $3(x-5)=12$. He said, "*I can rewrite this equation by distributing the 3 on the left-hand side.*" After distributing, what should his new equation be? Solve this equation using David's method.

10*81.   SOLVING BY UNDOING

Juan says, "I see the whole thing a different way." Here is how he explains his approach to solving $3(x-5)=12$, which he calls "undoing:" "*Instead of distributing first, I want to eliminate the 3 from the left side by undoing the multiplication.*"

a.   What can Juan do to both sides of the equation to remove the 3? Why does this work?

b.   Solve the equation using Juan's method. Did you get the same result as David?

c.   Why is it appropriate for this method to be called "undoing?"

10*82.   SOLVING BY LOOKING INSIDE

Kenya said, "I solved David's equation in a much quicker way!" She solved the equation $3(x-5)=12$ with an approach she calls "looking inside." Here is how she described her thinking: "*I think about everything inside the parentheses as a group. After all, the parentheses group all that stuff together. I think the contents of the parentheses must be 4.*"

a.   Why must the expression inside the parentheses equal four?

b.   Write an equation that states that the contents of the parentheses must equal four. Then solve this equation. Did you get the same result as with David's method?

10*83.   THE THREE METHODS

a.   Find the Math Notes box at the end of this lesson and read it with your team.

b.   Match the names of approaches on the left with the examples on the right.

1. Rewriting	*i.* "If $3+(4n-4)=12$, then $(4n-4)$ must equal 9..."
2. Looking inside	*ii.* "Subtracting is the opposite of adding, so in the equation $3(x-7)+4=23$, I can start by subtracting four from both sides...."
3. Undoing	
	iii. "This problem might be easier if I turned $4(2x-3)$ into $8x-12$..."

10*84.   For each equation, decide whether it would be best to rewrite, look inside, or undo. Then solve the equation, showing your work and writing down the name of the approach you used. Check your solutions if possible.

a. $\frac{2x-8}{10}=6$ b. $4+(x\div3)=9$ c. $\sqrt{3x+3}=6$

d. $8-(2x+1)=3$ e. $\sqrt{x}+4=9$ f. $\frac{x}{3}-\frac{x}{9}=6$

10*85. Consider the equation $(x-7)^2 = 9$.

    a.   Solve this equation using *all three* approaches studied in this lesson. Make sure each group member solves the equation using all three approaches.

    b.   Did you get the same solution using all three approaches? If not, why not?

    c.   Of the three methods, which do you think was the most efficient method for this problem? Why?

METHODS AND MEANINGS

MATH NOTES

Methods to Solve One-Variable Equations

Here are three different approaches you can take to solve a one-variable equation:

Rewriting: Use algebraic techniques to rewrite the equation. This will often involve using the Distributive Property to get rid of parentheses. Then solve the equation using solution methods you know.

$$5(x-1) = 15$$
$$5x - 5 = 15$$
$$5x = 20$$
$$x = 4$$

Looking Inside: Choose a part of the equation that includes the variable and is grouped together by parentheses or another symbol. (Make sure it includes *all* occurrences of the variable!) Ask yourself, "What must this part of the equation equal to make the equation true?" Use that information to write and solve a new, simpler equation.

$$5(x-1) = 15$$
$$5(\ 3\ ) = 15$$
$$x - 1 = 3$$
$$x = 4$$

Undoing: Start by undoing the *last* operation was that done to the variable. This will give you a simpler equation, which you can solve either by undoing again or with some other approach.

$$\frac{5(x-1)}{5} = \frac{15}{5}$$
$$x - 1 = 3$$
$$\underline{+1 = +1}$$
$$x = 4$$

10*86. Read the statements made by Hank and Frank below.

Hank says, "The absolute value of 5 is 5."

Frank says, "The absolute value of –5 is 5."

a. Is Hank correct? Is Frank correct?

b. How many different values for x make the equation $|x| = 5$ true?

10*87. Find all possible values for x in each of the following equations.

a. $|x| = 4$ b. $|x| = 100$

c. $|x| = -3$ d. $|x - 2| = 5$

10*88. Which of the expressions below are equal to 1? (Note: More than one answer is possible!)

a. $\frac{2x+3}{3+2x}$ b. $\frac{6x-12}{6(x-2)}$ c. $\frac{(2x-3)(x+2)}{2x^2+x-6}$ d. $\frac{x}{2} \div \frac{2}{x}$

10*89. Solve the inequalities below. Show your solution on a number line.

a. $8 + 3x > 2$ b. $\frac{2}{3}x - 6 \le 2$

c. $-2x - 1 < -3$ d. $\frac{5}{x} \le \frac{1}{3}$

10*90. For the equation $\frac{3}{200} + \frac{x}{50} = \frac{7}{100}$.

a. Find a <u>simpler</u> equivalent equation (i.e., an equivalent equation with no fractions) and solve for x.

b. Which method listed in this lesson's Math Notes Box did you use?

10*91. Mr. Nguyen has decided to divide $775 among his three daughters. If the oldest gets twice as much as the youngest, and the middle daughter gets $35 more than the youngest, how much does each child get? Write an equation and solve. Be sure to identify your variables.

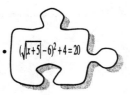

So far in this course you have seen many types of equations that have no solution, one solution, two solutions, and even infinitely many solutions! Is there any way to predict how many solutions an equation will have without solving it? Today you will focus on this question as you study quadratic equations written in perfect square form and equations with absolute value. As you work with your team, ask yourself the following questions:

Is there another way?

How do I see it?

Did I find <u>all</u> possible solutions?

10*92. The quadratic equation below is written in **perfect square form**. It is called this because the term $(x-3)^2$ forms a square when built with tiles. Solve this quadratic equation using one of the methods studied in Lesson 10.2.1.

$$(x-3)^2 = 12$$

    a.   How many solutions did you find?

    b.   Write your answer in **exact** form. That is, write it in a form that is precise and does not have any rounded decimals.

    c.   Write your answer in **approximate** form. Round your answers to the nearest hundredth (0.01).

10*93. THE NUMBER OF SOLUTIONS

The equation in problem 10*92 had two solutions. However, from your prior experience you know that some quadratic equations have no solutions and some have only one solution. How can we quickly determine how many solutions a quadratic equation has?

With your team, solve equations (a) through (f) below. Express your answers in both **exact form** and **approximate form**. Look for patterns among those that have no solution and those that have only one solution. Be ready to report your patterns to the class.

    a. $(x+4)^2 = 20$ b. $(7x-5)^2 = -2$ c. $(2x-3)^2 = 49$

    d. $(5-10x)^2 = 0$ e. $(x+2)^2 = -10$ f. $(x+11)^2 + 5 = 5$

10*94. Use the patterns you found in problem 10*93 to determine quickly how many solutions each quadratic below has. You do not need to solve the equations.

    a. $(5m-2)^2 + 6 = 0$ b. $(4+2n)^2 = 0$ c. $11 = (7+2x)^2$

10*95.   Consider the equation $|2x - 5| = 9$.

   a.   How many solutions do you think this equation has? Why?

   b.   Which of the three solution approaches do you think will work best on this equation?

   c.   With your team, solve $|2x - 5| = 9$. Record your work carefully as you go. Check your solution(s).

10*96.   The equation $|2x - 5| = 9$ from problem 10*95 had two solutions. Do you think all absolute value equations must have two solutions? Consider this as you answer the questions below.

   a.   Can an absolute value equation have no solution? With your team, create an absolute value equation that has <u>no</u> solution. How can you be sure there is no solution?

   b.   Likewise, create an equation with an absolute value that will have only <u>one</u> solution. **Justify** why it will have only one solution.

10*97.   Is there a **connection** between how to tell the number of solutions of a quadratic in perfect square form and how to tell the number of solutions of an equation with an absolute value? In a Learning Reflection, describe this connection and explain how you can determine how many solutions both types of equations have. Be sure to include examples for each. Title this reflection "Number of Solutions" and include today's date.

ETHODS AND MEANINGS

Perfect Square Form of a Quadratic

MATH NOTES

When a quadratic equation is written as a quantity squared, such as the one below, we say it is in **perfect square form**. Notice that when the quadratic expression on the left is built with tiles it forms a square, as shown at right.

$$(x + 3)^2 = 25$$

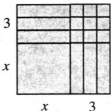

10*98.   Solve these equations, if possible. Each time, be sure you have found all possible
          solutions. Check your work and write down the name of the method(s) you used.

    a. $(x+4)^2 = 49$ b. $3\sqrt{x+2} = 12$

    c. $\frac{2}{x} + \frac{3}{10} = \frac{13}{10}$ d. $5(2x-1) - 2 = 13$

10*99.   Is $x = -4$ a solution to $\frac{1}{3}(2x+5) > -1$? Explain how you know.

10*100.   Multiply or divide the rational expressions below. Leave your answer in simplified
          form. Assume the denominators do not equal zero.

    a. $\frac{(x+4)(2x-1)(x-7)}{(x+8)(2x-1)(3x-4)} \div \frac{(4x-3)(x-7)}{(x+8)(3x-4)}$ b. $\frac{2m^2+7m-15}{m^2-16} \cdot \frac{m^2-6m+8}{2m^2-7m+6}$

10*101.   Factor each of the following expressions <u>completely</u>. Be sure to look for any common
          factors.

    a. $4x^2 - 12x$ b. $3y^2 + 6y + 3$

    c. $2m^2 + 7m + 3$ d. $3x^2 + 4x - 4$

10*102.   The diagram at right shows one way to represent the fraction $\frac{1}{7}$.

    a.   Draw a similar diagram to represent $\frac{3}{7}$.

    b.   What is $\frac{1}{7} + \frac{3}{7}$? Use your diagram to **justify** your answer.

    c.   Use a new diagram to add $\frac{2}{9} + \frac{8}{9}$.

10*103.   Rewrite each of the expressions below. Avoid leaving negative exponents in your
          solution.

    a. $\left(\frac{2x}{y^2}\right)^2$ b. $\left(6x^3\right)\left(3x^{-1}y\right)$ c. $\frac{(xy)^{-1}}{(x^2y^3)^{-1}}$

10.2.3 Which method is best?

More Solving and an Application

$(\sqrt{|x+5|} - 6)^2 + 4 = 20$

Recently you investigated three different approaches to solving one-variable equations: rewriting, looking inside, and undoing. Today you will use those approaches to solve new kinds of equations you have not solved before. You will also use your equation writing skills to write an inequality for an application. As you work today, ask yourself these questions:

How can I represent it?

What is the best approach for this equation?

Have I found all the solutions?

10*104. Solve these equations. Each time, be sure you have found all possible solutions. Check your work and write down the name of the method(s) you used.

a. $|x + 1| = 5$

b. $(x - 13)^3 = 8$

c. $2\sqrt{x - 4} = 14$

d. $|4x + 20| = 8$

e. $3(x + 12)^2 = 27$

f. $6|x - 8| = 18$

10*105. RUB A DUB DUB

Ernie is thinking of installing a new hot-tub in his backyard. The company he will order it from makes square hot-tubs, and the smallest tub he can order is 4 feet by 4 feet. He plans to add a three-foot wide deck on two adjacent sides, as shown in the diagram at left. If Ernie's backyard (also a square) has 169 square feet of space, what are the possible dimensions that his hot-tub can be? Write and solve an inequality that represents this situation. Be sure to define your variable.

METHODS AND MEANINGS

MATH NOTES

Solving Absolute Value Equations

To solve an equation with an absolute value algebraically, first determine the possible values of the quantity inside the absolute value.

For example, if $|2x + 3| = 7$, then the quantity $(2x + 3)$ must equal 7 or -7.

With these two values, set up new equations and solve as shown at right.

$$|2x + 3| = 7$$

$$2x + 3 = 7 \quad \text{or} \quad 2x + 3 = -7$$
$$2x = 10 \qquad\qquad 2x = -10$$
$$x = 5 \qquad\qquad x = -5$$

Always check your solutions by substituting them into the original equation:

Test x = 2: $|2(2) + 3| = 7$ True   Test x = - 5: $|2(-5) + 3| = 7$ True

10*106.   Sketch a graph of the inequality below. Shade the region containing the solutions of the inequality.

$$y > (x-4)(x+3)$$

10*107.   Jessie looked at the equation $(x-11)^2 = -4$ and stated, "This quadratic has no solutions!" How did she know?

10*108.   Solve these equations, if possible. Each time, be sure you have found all possible solutions. Check your work and write down the name of the method(s) you used.

   a. $9(x-4)^2 = 81$ b. $|x-6| = 2$

   c. $5 = 2 + \sqrt{3x}$ d. $2|x+1| = -4$

10*109.   Review what you know about solving inequalities by solving those below. Show your solutions on a number line.

   a. $6x - 1 < 11$ b. $\frac{1}{3}x \geq 2$

   c. $9(x-2) > 18$ d. $5 - \frac{x}{4} \leq \frac{1}{2}$

10*110.   Examine the rectangle formed by the tiles shown at right. Write the area of the rectangle as a product and a sum.

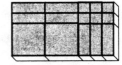

10*111.   Multiply or divide the rational expressions below. Leave your answer in simplified form. Assume the denominators do not equal zero.

   a. $\dfrac{(x-3)^2}{2x-1} \cdot \dfrac{2x-1}{(3x-14)(x+6)} \cdot \dfrac{x+6}{x-3}$ b. $\dfrac{4x^2+5x-6}{3x^2+5x-2} \div \dfrac{4x^2+x-3}{6x^2-5x+1}$

10.2.4 How can I solve the inequality?

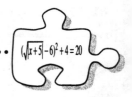

Solving Inequalities with Absolute Value

The three approaches you have for solving equations can also be used to solve inequalities. While the one-variable inequalities you solve today look different than the ones in Chapter 9, the basic process for solving will be similar. As you solve equations and inequalities in today's lesson, ask yourself these questions:

How can I represent it?

What is the connection?

10*112. Solve the inequality $2x+7<12$. Represent your solutions on a number line.

    a. What is the boundary point? Is it part of the solution? Why or why not?

    b. How do you find a boundary point? How do you find the solutions of an inequality after you have found the boundary point? Briefly review the process with your team.

10*113. Now consider the inequality $|x-2|>3$.

    a. Can you use the process from the previous problem to solve this inequality? How is it different from solving $|x-2|=3$? Solve the inequality and represent your solution on a number line.

    b. How was solving $|x-2|>3$ different from solving $2x+7<2$?

10*114. Examine the graph of $y=|x-2|$ and $y=3$ at right.

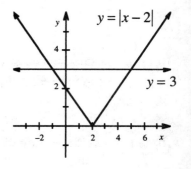

    a. How does this graph confirm your solution to $|x-2|>3$ from problem 10*112? Be prepared to explain your thinking.

    b. How would the solution change for the inequality $|x-2|\le 3$? Draw this solution on a number line. Explain how the graph above also confirms this solution.

    c. Now use the graph to predict the x-values that make $|x-2|\ge -1$ true.

10*115. Consider the quadratic inequality $x^2 + 2x + 1 < 4$.

   a. Solve for the boundary point(s). How many boundary points are there?

   b. Place the boundary point(s) on a number line. How many regions do you need to test?

   c. Test each region and determine which one(s) make the inequality true. Identify the solution region(s) on the number line.

   d. Confirm your solution by graphing $y = x^2 + 2x + 1$ and $y = 4$ on the same set of axes on graph paper. Highlight the portion of the graph which confirms your solution to part (c).

10*116. For today's Learning Reflection, summarize the process you used to solve inequalities algebraically today. (You do not have to discuss the graphical representation.) Then make up your own example problem and show how that problem is solved.

10*117. Rewrite each of the expressions below with no parentheses and no fractions. Negative exponents are acceptable in your answer.

   a. $\dfrac{4(9x^3)^2}{27x^8}$

   b. $\dfrac{(2mn^3)^{10}}{2^5 m^2 \cdot 2^4 m^{12} n^2}$

10*118. Determine the number of solutions for each of the quadratics below. Note: You do not need to solve the quadratics.

   a. $(x-2)^2 = -3$

   b. $6x^2 - x - 2 = 0$

   c. $4x^2 - 4x + 1 = 0$

   d. $427x^2 + 731x - 280 = 0$

10*119. Find the equation of the line parallel to $y = -\frac{2}{3}x - 7$ through the point (-6, 9).

10*120. Graph the system of inequalities below on graph paper. Carefully shade the region that represents the solution to both inequalities.

$$y \le -|x-2|+3$$
$$y \ge -1$$

10*121. Multiply or divide the expressions below. Leave your answer as simplified as possible.

a. $\dfrac{8x^2-12x-8}{2x^2-5x-3} \cdot \dfrac{x^2+2x-15}{6x-12}$

b. $\dfrac{7x^2+5x-2}{x^2+2x-8} \div \dfrac{3x^2-2x-5}{3x^2-11x+10}$

10*122. Solve the equations and inequalities below. Check your solution(s), if possible.

a. $300x - 1500 = 2400$

b. $\frac{3}{2}x = \frac{5}{6}x + 2$

c. $x^2 - 25 \le 0$

d. $|3x-2| > 4$

10.2.5 How can I solve this inequality?

· ·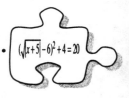

Solving Absolute Value and Quadratic Inequalities

Today we will finish our focus on solving equations and inequalities. By the end of the lesson today, you will have the tools to solve complex equations and inequalities.

10*123. At right is a graph showing $y = x^2 + x - 6$ and $y = 3x+2$. Use the graph to find the solutions for $x^2 + x - 6 \ge 3x+2$.

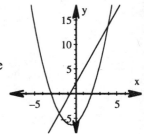

10*124. Solve these inequalities and represent your solution on a number line.

a. $|x+2| > 1$

b. $x^2 + x - 12 < 0$

c. $|2(x-1)| \ge 0$

d. $9x - 4 \le 6 - x$

e. $|3x-11| < -2$

f. $(x-2)^2 > 7$

10*125. FOG CITY

San Francisco is well known for its
fog: very thick, low-lying clouds that
hide its hills. One foggy day, Penelope
was practicing kicking a football on
the football field of her school. Once
she kicked the football so high that it
disappeared into the fog! If the height
of the ball (in feet) could be
represented at time t (in seconds) by
the equation $h(t) = -16t^2 + 96t$, and if
the fog was 140 feet off the ground,
during what times of its flight was the
ball not visible? Explain how you got
your answer.

10*126. TEAM SOLVING CHALLENGE

Now that you have the skills necessary to solve many interesting equations and
inequalities, work with your team to solve the inequality below. Show your solutions
on a number line and be prepared to share your solving process with the class.

$$\left(\sqrt{|x+5|} - 6\right)^2 + 4 \leq 20$$

Review & Preview

10*127. Rewrite each of the expressions below with no parentheses and no fractions. Negative
exponents are acceptable in your answer.

a. $(5a^{-2}b^3)^8 \cdot (5ab^{-2})^{-6}$

b. $\dfrac{15x^{-5}y^2}{(3x^2)^2 \cdot y^{-3}}$

10*128. How many solutions does the equation $|7 - 3x| + 1 = 0$ have? Explain how you know.

10*129.   Solve the equations and inequalities below. Represent each solution on a number line.

   a. $\sqrt{x-1}+13=13$ b. $6|x|>18$ c. $|3x-2|\le 2$

   d. $\frac{4}{5}-\frac{2x}{3}=\frac{3}{10}$ e. $(4x-2)^2 \le 100$ f. $(x-1)^3 = 8$

10*130.   On graph paper, graph a line through the point (4, -3) with a slope of $-\frac{2}{3}$.

   a.   Find the equation of the line.

   b.   Is this line perpendicular to the line $6x-4y=8$? Explain how you know.

10*131.   Simplify the rational expressions below as much as possible. Assume the denominators do not equal zero.

   a. $\dfrac{(x-4)^3(2x-1)}{(2x-1)(x-4)^2}$ b. $\dfrac{7m^2-22m+3}{3m^2-7m-6}$

   c. $\dfrac{(z+2)^9(4z-1)^7}{(z+2)^{10}(4z-1)^5}$ d. $\dfrac{(x+2)(x^2-6x+9)}{(x-3)(x^2-4)}$

10*132.   **Multiple Choice:** Which of the graphs below show the solutions for $y<-\frac{2}{5}x+1$?

   a.   b.

   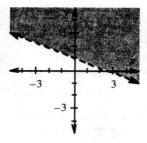

   c.   d.

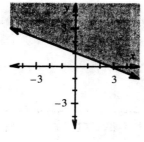   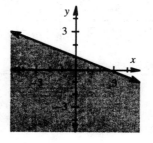

10.3.1 How can I make it a square?

Completing the Square

You have learned many ways to solve quadratic equations so far in this course. Sometimes, using the Quadratic Formula can be complicated and messy, while solving equations in perfect square form (such as $(x+2)^2 = 3$) can be very straightforward. Therefore, it is sometimes convenient to change a quadratic from standard form into perfect square form. One method that you will investigate in this lesson is called **completing the square**.

10*133.   Review what you know about solving quadratic equations as you solve the two equations below. Be ready to share your method(s) with the class.

    a. $x^2 + 4x + 1 = 0$ b. $(x+2)^2 = 3$

10*134.   With your team, and then with the class, discuss the following questions.

    a.   Examine the solutions to $x^2 + 4x + 1 = 0$ and $(x+2)^2 = 3$. What do you notice? What does this tell you about the two equations? Verify your conclusion algebraically.

    b.   Of all the methods used in problem 10*133, which was most efficient and straightforward?

10*135.   COMPLETING THE SQUARE

With your team, examine how the two different equations can be represented using tiles on an equation mat, shown below.

    a.   What "legal" move can be done to the equation $x^2 + 4x + 1 = 0$ that will result in the equation $(x+2)^2 = 3$?

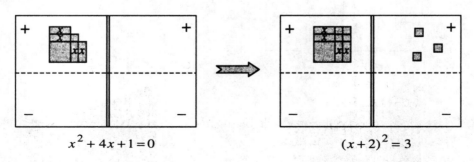

$$x^2 + 4x + 1 = 0 \qquad\qquad\qquad (x+2)^2 = 3$$

    b.   Why is this method called "completing the square"?

10*136. Use your observations from problem 10*135 to change the quadratics below into perfect square form. Then solve the resulting quadratics. Building the squares with algebra tiles may be useful. Record your work on the Resource Page provided by your teacher.

a.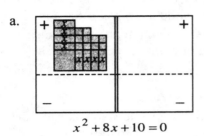

$$x^2 + 8x + 10 = 0$$

b.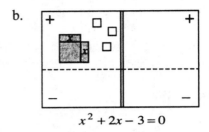

$$x^2 + 2x - 3 = 0$$

10*137. The problems below introduce different situations that can arise while completing the square. Carefully choose what to add to both sides of each equation below to change the quadratics into perfect square form. Then solve the resulting quadratic. Again, building the equations with algebra tiles may be useful. Record your work on the Resource Page provided by your teacher.

a.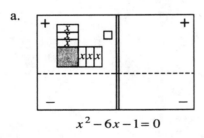

$$x^2 - 6x - 1 = 0$$

b.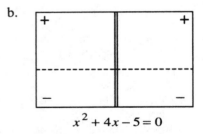

$$x^2 + 4x - 5 = 0$$

c.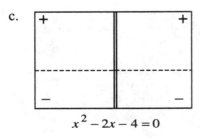

$$x^2 - 2x - 4 = 0$$

10*138. Use tiles to change the quadratic below into perfect square form. Then solve the resulting quadratic equation.

METHODS AND MEANINGS

Forms of a Quadratic Equation

There are three main forms of a quadratic equation: standard form, factored form, and perfect square form. Study these examples below. Assume that $a \neq 0$ and that the meaning of a, b, and c are different for each form below.

Standard Form: Any quadratic written in the form $ax^2 + bx + c = 0$.

Factored Form: Any quadratic written in the form $a(x+b)(x+c) = 0$.

Perfect Square Form: Any quadratic written in the form $a(x+b)^2 = c$.

10*139.   Use your understanding of the number 1 to simplify the rational expressions below. Assume the denominators do not equal zero.

a. $\dfrac{(x-3)(2x+9)(4x-3)}{(2x+9)(5x+1)(x-3)}$

b. $\dfrac{25x^2+20x+4}{25x^2-4}$

c. $\dfrac{16x^2+24x+8}{2x^2-2x-4}$

d. $\dfrac{24xy^2}{36x^2y}$

10*140.   Solve the quadratic equation below **twice**: once using the Quadratic Formula and once by completing the square and solving the quadratic in perfect square form. You should get the same result using both methods. What happened?

$$x^2 + 6x + 11 = 0$$

10*141. Solve the inequalities and the equations below if possible. Represent your solution on a number line.

a. $|x| + 3 < 5$

b. $5(2x + 1) \geq 30$

c. $\frac{1}{x} - \frac{5}{2} = \frac{3}{2}$

d. $-5 - x > 3 - x$

e. $3\sqrt{4 - x} + 1 = 13$

f. $|x + 1| \leq 4$

10*142. Verify your solution to part (f) of 10*141 by graphing the functions below on the same set of axes. Highlight the portion(s) of the graph for which $|x + 1| \leq 4$.

$$y = |x + 1|$$
$$y = 4$$

10*143. Match each function below with its corresponding graph. Explain how you made your decision.

i. $y = \sqrt{x - 2} + 1$

ii. $y = x^3 + 1$

iii. $y = -|x - 2| + 1$

a.

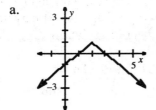

b.

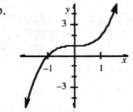

c.

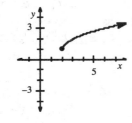

10*144. Add, subtract, multiply or divide the following rational expressions. Simplify your answer if possible. Assume the denominators do not equal zero.

a. $\dfrac{12x^2 + 4x - 1}{36x^2 - 12x + 1} \cdot \dfrac{x^2 - 64}{2x^2 + 17x + 8}$

b. $\dfrac{2}{3x} + \dfrac{4}{x^2}$

c. $\dfrac{x - 6}{x^2 - 4} - \dfrac{1}{x + 2}$

d. $\dfrac{2x^2 - 10x}{x^2 - 4} \div \dfrac{x^2 - 5x}{x^2 - 4x - 12}$

10.3.2 How can I generalize?

More Completing the Square

Today you will learn more about completing the square and will **generalize** how to complete the square for any quadratic in standard form.

10*145. Determine the number of solutions for each quadratic equation below by first completing the square using algebra tiles or drawing a diagram. Then explain how you can quickly determine how many solutions a quadratic equation has once it is written in perfect square form.

a. $x^2 - 6x + 7 = 0$

b. $m^2 + 1$

c. $p^2 + 2p + 1 = 0$

d. $k^2 - 4k + 9 = 0$

10*146. Examine the results of your work in problem 10*145 and look for ways to **generalize** the process of completing the square. In other words, how can you change a quadratic into perfect square form without using tiles or drawing a diagram? It may help to make a table like the one started below. Then answer the questions below.

Standard Form	Perfect Square Form
$x^2 - 6x + 7 = 0$	

a. Describe any patterns you find when comparing a quadratic written in standard form with its corresponding equation in perfect square form.

b. When a quadratic is changed to perfect square form, how can you predict what will be in the parentheses? For example, if you want to change $x^2 + 10x - 3 = 0$ into perfect square form, what will be the dimensions of the square?

c. To complete the square, you often need to add some unit tiles to both sides of the equation. How can you predict how many tiles will need to be added?

10*147. Use your generalized completing the square process to rewrite and solve each of these quadratic equations.

a. $k^2 - 16k - 17 = 0$

b. $x^2 + 5x + 4 = 0$

c. $w^2 + 28w + 52 = 0$

d. $z^2 - 1000z + 60775 = 0$

10*148. Which of the expressions below are equivalent to $16x^8$? Make sure you find *all* the correct answers!

    a. $(16x^4)^2$ b. $8x^2 \cdot 2x^6$

    c. $(2x^2)^4$ d. $(4x^4)^2$

    e. $(2x^4)^4$ f. $(\frac{1}{16}x^{-8})^{-1}$

10*149. What is the slope of the line passing through the points (4, –8) and (–3, 12)?

10*150. Use your generalized completing the square process to rewrite and solve each of these quadratic equations.

    a. $x^2 + 4x = -3$ b. $x^2 - 8x + 7 = 0$ c. $x^2 - 24x + 129 = 0$

10*151. Multiply or divide the rational expressions below. Leave your answer in simplified form. Assume the denominators do not equal zero.

    a. $\frac{4x^2+x-14}{3x^2-11x+6} \div \frac{4x-7}{x-3}$ b. $\frac{5x^2-8x-4}{x^2-9x-22} \cdot \frac{x^2-4}{5x^2+22x+8}$

10*152. Solve the following equations and inequalities, if possible. Represent your solution on a number line.

    a. $\frac{3}{9} - \frac{x}{3} = \frac{x}{5}$ b. $(3+x)^2 < 9$ c. $8|x+1| \geq 64$

    d. $11 - \sqrt{x+3} = 13$ e. $\frac{x}{8} = \frac{2}{x}$ f. $|x-5|+1 > 0$

10*153. On graph paper, graph the inequality $y \leq |x| + 2$.

① TEAM BRAINSTORM

With your team, brainstorm a list for each of the following topics. Be as detailed as you can. How long can you make your list? Challenge yourselves.

Topics: What have we studied in this chapter? What ideas and words were important in what we learned? Remember to be as detailed as you can.

Ways of Thinking: What ways of thinking have we used in this chapter? When did we use them?

Connections: What topics, ideas, and words we learned *before* this chapter are connected to the new ideas in this chapter? Again, make your list as long as you can.

Be prepared to share your team's ideas with the class.

② MAKING CONNECTIONS

The following is a list of all of the key words in this chapter. The words that appear in **bold** are new to this chapter. Make sure that you are familiar with all of these words.

absolute value	**base (p. 421)**	**completing the square (p. 447)**
boundary point	equation	equivalent equations
exponent (p. 421)	inequality	**fraction buster (p. 430)**
looking inside (p. 435)	number line	**perfect square form (p. 438, 449)**
quadratic	Quadratic Formula	**rational expression (p. 409, 424)**
rewriting (p. 435)	solution	standard form for quadratics
undoing (p. 435)		

Make a concept map showing all of the **connections** you can find between the key words and ideas listed above. For each key word or idea, sketch an example. Label each connection with a phrase explaining how the ideas are related. While you are making your map, you may think of related ideas that are not listed above. Be sure to include these ideas in your concept map.

③ SUMMARIZING MY UNDERSTANDING

This section gives you an opportunity to show what you know about one or more topics or ideas. Your teacher will give you directions for exactly how to do this.

④ WHERE AM I?

This section will help you evaluate which types of problems you have seen you feel comfortable with and which you need more help with. This section appears at the end of every chapter to help you check your understanding. Even if your teacher does not assign this section, it is a good idea to try the problems and find out for yourself what you know and what you need to work on.

Solve each problem as completely as you can. The table at the end of the closure section has answers to these problems. It also tells you where you can find additional help and practice on problems like these.

CL 10*1. Simplify the following expressions. Assume the denominators do not equal zero.

a. $\dfrac{x^2 y^3}{x y^2}$

b. $\dfrac{(x+2)^2(x-4)}{(x+2)(x-4)}$

c. $\dfrac{x^2-x-6}{x-3}$

d. $\dfrac{5x^2-2xy+7}{5x^2-2xy+7}$

e. $\dfrac{x^2-5x+4}{x^2-x-12}$

f. $\dfrac{x^2-25}{x^2+10x+25} \div \dfrac{x-5}{x+3}$

CL 10*2. To help her redecorate, Reyna made a small scale drawing of her apartment. Reyna's apartment is 120 inches wide. On her drawing, she made it 18 inches wide. Reyna found a 54-inch sofa at a garage sale. How long should the sofa be on her drawing?

CL 10*3. Solve the equations below using whatever method you wish. How many solutions does each problem have?

a. $\dfrac{6x-5}{2x+1} - \dfrac{2x-7}{2x+1} = 2$

b. $\sqrt{x-5}+10=15$

c. $|x-7|=22$

d. $(3x+7)^2 = 144$

e. $3(2x+1)^3 = 24$

f. $3x^2 - 25x = -28$

CL 10*4. Solve each inequality algebraically. Then represent your solution on a number line.

a. $5x-7 \geq 2x+5$

b. $6x-29 > 4x+12$

c. $x^2 \leq -4x+5$

d. $|2x-7| > 31$

CL 10*5. Solve each of these quadratic equations twice, once by completing the square and once by using the Quadratic Formula. Make sure you get the same answer using both methods!

a. $0 = x^2 - 10x + 21$
b. $x^2 + 14x + 54 = 0$

CL 10*6. Graph each system of inequalities and shade its solutions.

a.
$$y \leq \frac{2}{3}x - 7$$
$$y < -x + 4$$

b.
$$y > -x^2 + 9$$
$$y \geq x^2 - 9x - 22$$

CL 10*7. Mario and Antoine have been slowly reading *War and Peace* over the last few weeks, but a friend just told them that something exciting happens on page 475. Even though each boy is at a different place in the book, they decide to race to page 475.

a. After 2 hours of reading, Mario is on page 350 and Antoine is on page 425. Who will get to page 475 first? **Justify** your answer.

b. After 6 hours of reading, Mario is on page 450 and Antoine is on page 465. Who will get to page 475 first? **Justify** your answer.

c. What page was Mario on when they started the race? What page was Antoine on when they started?

d. At what rate does Mario read? At what rate does Antoine read?

e. *War and Peace* is 1400 pages long. If they keep reading, after how many hours will each boy finish the book?

CL 10*8. For the equation $y = \frac{5}{3}x + 7$, find:

a. The equation of the line that is parallel to the given line and passes through the point (3, 2).

b. The equation of the line that is perpendicular to the given line and passes through the point (10, 4).

CL 10*9. Rewrite each of these expressions. Your answer should have no parentheses and no negative exponents.

a. $4(2x^{-3}y^5)^4$

b. $\dfrac{10x^3y^{-4}}{25x^5y^2}$

c. $12x^{-10}y^{53}\cdot(3x^5y^{-10})^4$

d. $\dfrac{m^2}{m^{-8}}\cdot\dfrac{3m^5}{m^9}$

CL 10*10. Check your answers to each problem above using the table at the end of the closure section. Which problems did you feel confident about? Which problems were hard? Use the table to make a list of topics you need help on and a list of topics you need to practice more.

⑤ HOW AM I THINKING?

This course emphasizes the following five ways of thinking:

- Reversing processes (going in both directions)

- Justifying (explaining why)

- Generalizing (showing how it works for all cases)

- Making Connections (showing how it fits in with other ideas)

- Applying and/or extending our knowledge (thinking about how we use it or where it can go)

Choose three of these ways of thinking that you remember using while working in this chapter. For each way of thinking that you choose, show and explain where you used it and how you used it. Describe why thinking in this way helped you solve a particular problem or understand something new. (For instance, explain why we wanted to generalize in this particular case, or why it was useful to see these particular connections.) Be sure to include examples to demonstrate your thinking.

Problem	Solution	Need Help?	More Practice
CL 10*1	a. xy b. $x+2$ c. $x+2$ d. 1 e. $\frac{x-1}{x+3}$ f. $\frac{x+3}{x+5}$	MN p. 410, MN p. 424, MN p. 428	10*3, 10*4, 10*12, 10*17, 10*24, 10*40, 10*42, 10*49, 10*50, 10*54, 10*58, 10*65, 10*74, 10*100, 10*111, 10*121, 10*131, 10*139, 10*144, 10*151
CL 10*2	8.1 inches	Sections 5.2.1 and 5.2.2, MN p. 206	5*67, 5*68, 5*80, 5*82, 6*58, 7*7, 7*58
CL 10*3	a. There are an infinite number of solutions. b. $x = 30$ c. $x = 29$ or -15 d. $x = \frac{5}{3}$ or $x = -\frac{19}{3}$ e. $x = \frac{1}{2}$ f. $x = 7$ or $\frac{4}{3}$	MN p. 435, MN p. 440	10*20, 10*74, 10*84, 10*85, 10*86, 10*87, 10*93, 10*94, 10*95, 10*98, 10*104, 10*108, 10*129, 10*141
CL 10*4	a. $x \geq 4$ b. $x > 20.5$ c. $-5 \leq x \leq 1$ d. $x > 19$ or $x < -12$	MN p. 375, MN p. 385, Sections 10.2.4 and 10.2.5	10*109, 10*112, 10*113, 10*122, 10*124, 10*129, 10*141, 10*152

Problem	Solution	Need Help?	More Practice
CL 10*5	a. $x = 7$ or 3 b. no solution	MN p. 186, MN p. 328, MN p. 334, MN p. 337, MN p. 357, MN p. 364, MN p. 438, MN p. 449	10*20, 10*92, 10*93, 10*94, 10*133, 10*135, 10*136, 10*137, 10*138, 10*140, 10*145, 10*146, 10*147, 10*150
CL 10*6	a. b.	MN p. 393	10*18, 10*52, 10*67, 10*78, 10*106, 10*120, 10*132, 10*153
CL 10*7	a. Cannot be determined because we do not know which pages Mario and Antoine were on before they started racing. b. Mario and Antoine will get to page 475 at the same time. Each will arrive after another hour. c. Mario: p. 300 Antoine: p. 405 d. Mario: 25 pp. per hour Antoine: 10 pp. per hour e. Mario: 44 hours Antoine: 99.5 hours	Section 7.1.2	7*63, 7*66, 7*98, 9*43

Problem	Solution		Need Help?	More Practice
CL 10*8	a. $y = \frac{5}{3}x - 3$ b. $y = -\frac{3}{5}x + 10$		MN p. 295, Section 7.3.1, MN p. 307, MN p. 314	7*44, 7*45, 7*84, 7*87, 7*94, 7*107, 7*116, 8*101, 9*20, 9*77
CL 10*9	a. $\frac{64y^{20}}{x^{12}}$ c. $972y^{13}x^{10}$	b. $\frac{2}{5x^2y^6}$ d. $3m^6$	MN p. 420	10*6, 10*12, 10*13, 10*14, 10*17, 10*23, 10*24, 10*26, 10*27, 10*31, 10*45, 10*53, 10*63, 10*103, 10*117, 10*127, 10*148

11

FUNCTIONS AND RELATIONS

CHAPTER 11 Functions and Relations

So far in this course you have studied linear and quadratic functions extensively. In this chapter, you will explore new non-linear functions and learn how to describe a function completely. You will get to know the shapes and behaviors of many different functions and will be able to distinguish them by their graphs and rules. Many of the functions we will study will look familiar to you because they relate closely to equations you have already learned to solve.

In this chapter, you will learn:

➤ How to find the domain and range of a function.

➤ How to recognize symmetry in a graph.

➤ How to determine if a relation is a function or not by looking at its table or graph.

➤ How to predict the shape of a graph by its rule.

➤ How to recognize the possible rule of a function by its graph.

➤ How different parameters in an equation affect the placement and direction of a graph.

Guiding Questions

Think about these questions throughout this chapter:

What does the graph look like?

Can you see a pattern?

How does it change?

How does it grow?

Is it a function?

How can you describe it?

Chapter Outline

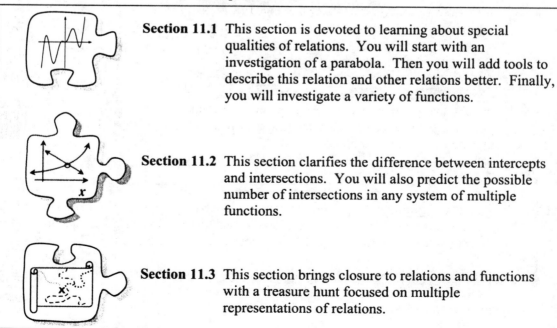

Section 11.1 This section is devoted to learning about special qualities of relations. You will start with an investigation of a parabola. Then you will add tools to describe this relation and other relations better. Finally, you will investigate a variety of functions.

Section 11.2 This section clarifies the difference between intercepts and intersections. You will also predict the possible number of intersections in any system of multiple functions.

Section 11.3 This section brings closure to relations and functions with a treasure hunt focused on multiple representations of relations.

11.1.1 How can we describe a function?

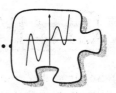

Describing a Function

What does it mean to describe a function completely? Today you will graph and investigate a new function: $y = \sqrt{x}$.

11*1.   **DESCRIBING A FUNCTION**

Your teacher will assign your team one of the rules below. On graph paper, graph your rule for x-values between –3 and 9. When your team is convinced that your graph is correct, discuss all the ways you can describe this graph. Then write as many summary statements about the graph as you can, such as, "*We noticed that as x gets larger, …*"

Relation list:

$$f(x) = \sqrt{x} \qquad\qquad f(x) = \sqrt{x-1} + 3$$

$$f(x) = \sqrt{x} + 1 \qquad\qquad f(x) = -\sqrt{x}$$

$$f(x) = \sqrt{x+2} - 1 \qquad\qquad f(x) = -\sqrt{x} - 2$$

11*2.   **PRESENT YOUR FINDINGS**

With your team, create a poster that contains not only the graph of your rule but also all of your observations and summary statements from problem 11*1. Be thorough and complete. Remember that a main goal of this activity is to determine what items a "complete description" of a relation must contain, so be sure to include everything you can. Be prepared to present your poster to the class. Remember to give reasons for all statements that you make.

11*3.   As a class, examine the posters that were presented by the teams. Create a list of all the ways to describe a function. Then, next to each description, create a question that will prompt you to look for this quality in other relations you encounter.

Once your list is complete, copy the questions into your Learning Reflection. Title this entry "Relation Investigation Questions" and include today's date.

11*4.   Find the dimensions of the generic rectangle shown at right and write its area as a sum and a product.

$-6x$	4
$9x^2$	$-6x$

11*5.   After noon, the number of people in Mal-wart grows steadily until 6:00 PM. If the equation $y = 228 + 58x$ represents the number of people in the store x hours after noon:

a.   How many people were in the store at noon?

b.   At what rate is the number of shoppers growing?

c.   When were there 402 shoppers in the store?

11*6.   Find the following absolute values.

a. $|0.75|$ b. $|-99|$ c. $|4 - 2 \cdot 3|$ d. $|\pi|$

11*7.   Jacob discovered that the x-intercepts of a certain parabola are $(3, 0)$ and $(-1, 0)$, but now he needs to find the vertex. Can you get him started? What do you know about the vertex? Draw a sketch of this parabola to help you.

11*8.   When a family with two adults and three children bought tickets for an amusement park, they paid a total of $56.50. The next family in line, with four children and one adult, paid $49.50. Find the adult and child ticket prices by writing a system of equations.

11*9.   Find the slope (m) and y-intercept (b) for each line below.

a. $2x + 7y = 14$ b. $y = 6 - \frac{x}{3}$ c. $y = \frac{10x - 2}{2}$ d. $y = 3x$

11*10.   Solve the following inequalities for x.

   a. $4x - 1 \geq 7$

   b. $3 - 2x < x + 6$

   c. $2(x - 5) \leq 8$

   d. $\frac{1}{2}x > 5$

11*11.   Javier thinks that $2^5 = 10$, while his brother Jesus thinks that $2^5 = 32$.

   a.   Who is correct and why?

   b.   Find 6^3 and 10^4.

11*12.   Match each graph below with the correct inequality.

   a. $y > -x + 2$ b. $y < 2x - 3$ c. $y \geq \frac{1}{2}x$ d. $y \leq -\frac{2}{3}x + 2$

   1) 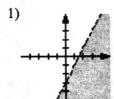   2) 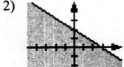   3) 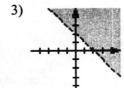   4)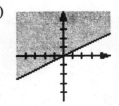

11*13.   Simplify by factoring and looking for fractions that are equivalent to 1. Assume the denominators do not equal zero.

   a. $\frac{(x+4)^2}{(x+4)(x-2)}$

   b. $\frac{8(x+2)^2(x-3)^3}{4(x+2)^3(x-3)^5}$

   c. $\frac{6(3x-1)^3}{3(3x-1)^2(x+4)}$

   d. $\frac{x^2+3x}{x^2+6x+9}$

11*14.   For the parabola $y = 2x^2 - 7x + 3$:

   a.   Give the coordinates of the y-intercept.

   b.   Give the coordinates of the two x-intercepts. Explain how you found your solution.

11*15.   Simplify each expression using the laws of exponents.

   a. $(x^2)(x^2y^3)$

   b. $\frac{x^3y^4}{x^2y^3}$

   c. $(2x^2)(-3x^4)$

   d. $(2x)^3$

11.1.2 What's the relationship?

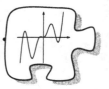

Relation Machines

In the next few lessons you will add to your list of what you can ask about a function. Throughout this course, you have used rules that relate two variables (like $y = -2x^2 + 11x + 1$) to make graphs and find information. Today you will look more closely at how rules that relate two variables help establish a relationship between the variables. You will also learn a new notation to help represent these relationships.

11*16.   ARE WE RELATED?

Examine the table of input (x) and output (y) values below. Is there a relationship between the input and output values? If so, state the relationship.

x	−3	−2	−1	0	1	2	3
y	8	3	0	−1	0	3	8

11*17.   RELATION MACHINES

Each equation that relates inputs to outputs is called a **relation**. This is easy to remember because the equation helps us know how all the y-values (outputs) on our graph are **related** to their corresponding x-values (inputs).

A relation works like a machine, as shown in the diagram at right. A relation is given a name that can be a letter, such as "f" or "g." The notation $f(x)$ represents the output when x is processed by the machine. (Note: $f(x)$ is read, "f of x.") When you put x into the machine, $f(x)$, the value of a function for a specific x-value, is what comes out.

Numbers are put into the relation machine (in this case, $f(x) = x^2 - 1$) one at a time and then the relation performs the operation(s) on each input to determine each output. For example, when $x = 3$ is put into the relation $f(x) = x^2 - 1$, the relation squares it and then subtracts one to get the output, which is 8. The notation $f(3) = 8$ shows that the relation named "f" connects the input (3) with the output (8).

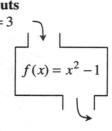

inputs

$x = 3$

$f(x) = x^2 - 1$

$f(3) = 8$

outputs

a.   Find the output for $f(x) = x^2 - 1$ when the input is $x = 4$, that is, find $f(4)$.

b.   Likewise, find $f(-1)$ and $f(10)$.

c.   If the output of this relation is 24, what was the input? That is, if $f(x) = 24$, then what is x? Is there more than one possible input?

11*18. Find the relationship between x and $f(x)$ in the table below and complete the relation.

x	9	1	100	4	49		0	25	20
$f(x)$		1			7	4		5	

Relation: $f(x) =$ _____

11*19. Find the corresponding outputs or inputs for the following relations. If there is no possible output for the given input, explain why not.

a. $x = -3$

$f(x) = -2x + 4$

$f(x) = ?$

b. $x = -2$

$f(x) = \sqrt{x+3}$

$f(x) = ?$

c. $x = 5$

$f(x) = x^3$

$f(x) = ?$

d. $x = -2$

$f(x) = \sqrt{x} + 1$

$f(x) = ?$

e. $x = 2$

$f(x) = \frac{x+3}{2x-5}$

$f(x) = ?$

f. $x = ?$

$f(x) = x^2 - 1$

$f(x) = 99$

g. $x = ?$

$f(x) = |x|$

$f(x) = -3$

h. $x = -4$

$f(x) = |x - 2|$

$f(x) = ?$

i. $x = -4$

$f(x) = |x| - 2$

$f(x) = ?$

11*20. Examine the relation machine defined at right. Notice that $g(1) = -1$, that is, when x is 1, the output (y, or $g(1)$) is –1.

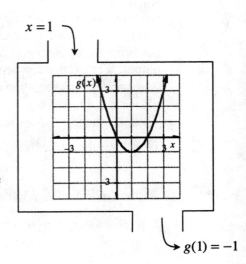

a. What is the output of the relation when the input is 2? That is, find $g(2)$.

b. Likewise, what are $g(-1)$ and $g(0)$?

c. What is the input of this relation when the output is 1? In other words, find x when $g(x) = 1$. Is there more than one possible solution?

11*21. If $f(x) = x^2$, then $f(4) = 4^2 = 16$. Find:

   a. $f(1)$ 　　　　　 b. $f(-3)$ 　　　　　 c. $f(t)$

11*22. Find the equation of the line with slope $m = -\frac{4}{3}$ that passes through the point $(12, -4)$.

11*23. Marley thinks that the two lines below are perpendicular but Bob thinks they are not. Who is correct and how do you know?

$$2x - 7y = 16$$
$$7x + 2y = 3$$

11*24. Ten minutes after he left his home, Gerald was 40 miles from his grandmother's house. Then, 22 minutes after he left, he was 34 miles from her house. If he was traveling toward his grandmother's home at a constant rate and reached her house after 90 minutes, how far away from her house does he live?

11*25. Use your method for multiplying and dividing fractions to simplify the expressions below. Assume the denominators do not equal zero.

   a. $\frac{x+2}{x-1} \cdot \frac{x-1}{x-6}$

   b. $\frac{(x-6)^2}{(2x+1)(x-6)} \cdot \frac{x(2x+1)(x+7)}{(x-1)(x+7)}$

   c. $\frac{(4x-3)(x+2)}{(x-5)(x-3)} \div \frac{(x-1)(x-3)}{(x-1)(x+2)}$

   d. $\frac{(x+3)(2x-5)}{(3x-4)(x-7)} \div \frac{(2x-5)}{(3x-4)}$

   e. $\frac{3x-1}{x+4} \div \frac{x-5}{x+4}$

   f. $\frac{x-3}{x+4} \cdot \frac{3x-10}{x+11} \cdot \frac{x+4}{3x-10}$

11*26. Write each expression without negative or zero exponents.

   a. 4^{-1} 　　 b. 7^0 　　 c. 5^{-2} 　　 d. x^{-2}

11.1.3 Is it predictable?

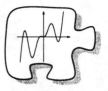

Functions

You have studied relations and have learned that each relation defines a relationship between the input and output values. But what happens when our relation gives us unpredictable results? That is, what happens when we cannot predict the output for a given input? Today you will study this situation and will be introduced to a special type of relation called a *function*.

11*27.　　THE COLA MACHINE

The cola machine at your school offers several types of soda. There are two buttons for your favorite drink, *Blast!*, while the other drinks (*Slurp, Lemon Twister*, and *Diet Slurp*) each have one button.

a.　Explain how the cola machine is a relation.

b.　Describe the input and output of this soda machine.

c.　While buying a soda, Ms. Whitney pushed the button for *Lemon Twister* and got a can of *Lemon Twister*. Later she went back to the same machine but this time pushing the *Lemon Twister* button got her a can of *Blast!* Is the machine functioning consistently? Why or why not?

d.　When Brandi pushed the top button for *Blast!* she received a can of *Blast!* Her friend, Miguel, decided to be different and pushed the second button for *Blast!* He, too, received a can of *Blast!* Is the machine functioning consistently? Why or why not?

e.　When Loutfi pushed a button for *Slurp*, he received a can of *Lemon Twister*! Later, Tayeisha also pushed the *Slurp* button and received a can of *Lemon Twister*. Still later, Tayeisha noticed that everyone else who pushed the *Slurp* button received a *Lemon Twister*. Is the machine functioning consistently? Explain why or why not.

f.　When a relation is functioning consistently and predictably, we call that relation a **function**. What is the main difference between a relation that is a function and a relation that is not a function?

11*28.　　Using your own words, write a definition of a function. Be prepared to share your definition with the class.

11*29.   Examine each of the relations below. Compare the inputs and outputs of each relation and decide if the relation is a function. Explain your reasoning. Use your definition of a function (from problem 11*28) to help you **justify** your conclusion.

a.

Button Number	1	1	2	4	2	3
Type of Candy	Stix	Stix	M&Ns	M&Ns	Duds	Duds

b.

x	7	-2	0	4	9	-3	6
$f(x)$	6	-3	4	2	10	-3	0

c.

x	3	-1	2	0	1	2	9
$g(x)$	4	-5	9	7	4	-8	2

d.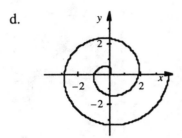

e.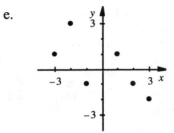

f.

x	$h(x)$
-8	11
4	3
11	-8
6	3
-8	11

g.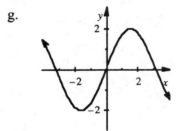

11*30.   Jade noticed that the line graphed at right is a function. "Hey—I think all lines are functions!" she exclaimed. Is she correct? Support your claim with a diagram.

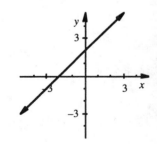

11*31.   In your Learning Reflection, describe what it means for a relationship to be a **function**. Think of another type of machine that you use on a regular basis and describe how it also operates as a function. Title this entry "Functions" and include today's date.

11*32.   If $g(x) = \sqrt{x-7}$, find $g(8)$, $g(32)$, and $g(80)$.

11*33.   Solve the system of equations below using any method. Be sure to check your solution.

$$5u + 6v = 2$$
$$u - 2v = 10$$

11*34.   Solve each equation below. Check each solution.

   a. $6 - (3 + x) = 10$ b. $100(x + 3) = 200$

   c. $\frac{1}{3}x + 4 = x - 2$ d. $\frac{4}{5} = \frac{x+2}{45}$

11*35.   Solve for x. Use any method. Check your solutions by testing them in the original equation.

   a. $|x - 3| = 5$ b. $5|x| = 35$

   c. $|x + 1| = 2$ d. $|x + 3| - 6 = -4$

11*36.   Find the equation of the line that goes through the points (9, 2) and (6, –1).

11*37.   **Multiple Choice:** Which line below is parallel to $y = \frac{-2}{3}x + 5$?

   a. $2x - 3y = 6$ b. $2x + 3y = 6$ c. $3x - 2y = 6$ d. $3x + 2y = 6$

11.1.4 What can go in? What can come out?
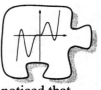

Domain and Range

So far we have described relations using intercepts and symmetry. We also have noticed that sometimes relations are functions. Today we are going to finish our focus on relations by describing the inputs and outputs of relations.

11*38.   Examine the graph of the relation $h(x)$ at right. Use it to estimate:

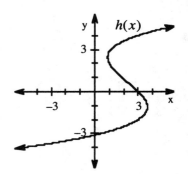

a. $h(3)$ b. $h(1)$

c. $h(-4)$ d.   Is this relation a function? Why or why not?

11*39.   Examine the relation shown at right.

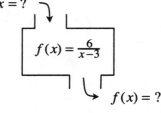

a.   Find $f(-3)$, $f(0)$, and $f(2)$.

b.   Find $f(3)$. What happened?

c.   Are there any other numbers that cannot be evaluated by this relation? In other words, are there any other values that cannot be x? Explain how you know.

d.   The set of numbers that can be used for x in a relation is called the **domain** of the relation. The domain is a description or list of all the possible x-values for the relation. Describe the domain of $f(x) = \frac{6}{x-3}$.

11*40.   Now examine $g(x)$ graphed at right.

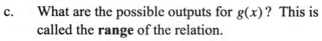

a.   Is $g(x)$ a function? How can you tell?

b.   Which x-values have points on the graph? That is, describe the domain of $g(x)$.

c.   What are the possible outputs for $g(x)$? This is called the **range** of the relation.

d.   Ricky thinks the range of $g(x)$ is: $-1, 0, 1, 2$, and 3. Is he correct? Why or why not?

11*41.   Chiu loves tables! He has decided to make the table below
          for a relation $f(x)$ to help him find its domain and range.

x	-3	-2	-1	0	1	2	3
$f(x)$	5	0	-3	-4	-3	0	5

   a.   From his table, can you tell what the domain of $f(x)$
         is? Why or why not?

   b.   From the table, can you tell the range of $f(x)$? Why or
         why not?

   c.   Is using a table a good way to determine the domain and range of a relation?

11*42.   Daniel is thinking about the relation shown at right.

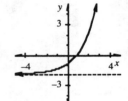

   a.   He noticed that the curve continues in both directions. What
         is the domain of this relation?

   b.   He found out that the dotted line represents a boundary that
         the graph gets closer to but never touches or crosses. How
         should he describe the range?

11*43.   FINDING DOMAIN AND RANGE

          The domain and range are good descriptors of a relation because they help us know
          what numbers can go into and come out of a relation. The domain and range can also
          help us set up useful axes when graphing and help us describe special points on a graph
          (such as a missing point or the lowest point).

          Work with your team to describe in words the domain and range of each relation below.

   a.
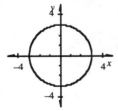

   b.
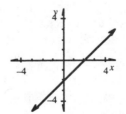

   c.
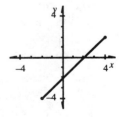

   d.
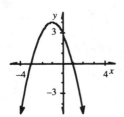

   e.
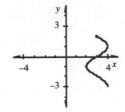

   f.
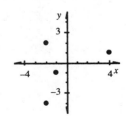

11*44.   TEAM CHALLENGE

Sketch the graph of a relation that has a domain of all the numbers greater than or equal to –2 and a range of all the numbers less than or equal to 3. Is there more than one possible answer?

METHODS AND MEANINGS

Relations and Functions

A **relation** establishes a correspondence between its inputs and outputs (in math language called "sets"). For equations, it establishes the relationship between two variables and determines one variable when given the other. Some examples of relations are:

$$y = x^2, \quad y = \tfrac{x}{x+3}, \quad y = -2x + 5$$

Since the value of y usually depends on x, y is often referred to as the **dependent variable**, while x is called the **independent variable**.

The set of possible inputs of a relation is called the **domain**, while the set of all possible outputs of a relation is called the **range**. For example, notice that all the points on the graph at right have x-values that are greater than or equal to –3. The arrows on the graph indicate that the graph will continue to expand to the right. Thus, the entire domain is the set of numbers that are greater than or equal to –3. Likewise, since each y-value has a corresponding point on the graph, then the range is the set of all numbers. This is also referred to as the set of **all real numbers**. In the future, this course will refer to these as "all numbers."

A **relation** is called a **function** if there exists <u>no more than one</u> output for each input. If a relation has two or more outputs for a single input value, it is not a function. For example, the relation graphed above is not a function because there are two y-values for each x-value greater than –3.

Functions are often given names, most commonly "f," "g," or "h." The notation $f(x)$ represents the output of a function, named "f" when x is the input. It is read "f of x." The notation $g(2)$, read "g of 2," represents the output of function g when $x = 2$. In the example at right, $f(2) = 10$.

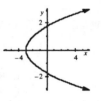

The function $y = 3x + 4$ and $f(x) = 3x + 4$ represent the <u>same function</u>. Notice that this notation is interchangeable; that is, $y = f(x)$.

11*45.   Which of the relations below are functions? If a relation is not a function, give a reason to support your conclusion.

a.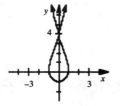

b.

x	y
−3	19
5	19
19	0
0	−3

c.

x	7	−2	0	7	4
y	10	0	10	3	0

d.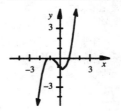

11*46.   Find the *x*- and *y*-intercepts for the relations in problem 11*45.

11*47.   Marisol and Mimi walked the same distance from their home to a shopping mall. Marisol walked 2 miles per hour, while Mimi left 1 hour later and walked 3 miles per hour. If they reached the mall at the same time, how far from the mall do they both live?

11*48.   A line passes through the points A(−3, −2) and B(2, 1). Does it also pass through the point C(5, 3)? **Justify** your conclusion.

11*49.   Solve each equation below for the indicated variable.

a. $3x - 2y = 18$ for x

b. $3x - 2y = 18$ for y

c. $rt = d$ for r

d. $C = 2\pi r$ for r

11*50.   Simplify each expression below.

a. $\dfrac{3x^2+8x+5}{x^2-5x-6} \cdot \dfrac{2x-5}{3x+5}$

b. $\dfrac{x^2+x-12}{x^2-x-6} \div \dfrac{x-5}{x^2-3x-10}$

11.1.5 What do we know about this relation?

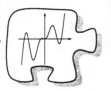

Investigating a New Relation

You are now familiar with the graphs of lines, parabolas, and square roots. What other types of relations can we study? Today you will use the questions your class generated in Lesson 11.1.1 to investigate several new relations. Your team will then report its findings to the class. Pay close attention to presentations! You will learn about several new and interesting relations.

11*51.   NEW RELATIONS

Your teacher will assign your team a new relation from the list below. On graph paper, carefully graph your new relation. Be sure to include enough values in your table to show any unusual behavior of your graph. Then use your list of questions about relations to investigate your particular relation.

Write clear summary statements that describe your relation. Create a team poster for your relation with a graph and any observations and statements your team made. Be ready to present your poster to the class.

Relation list:

$$f(x) = \frac{1}{x} \qquad\qquad\qquad f(x) = x^3$$

$$f(x) = \frac{1}{x^2} \qquad\qquad\qquad f(x) = 0.5^x$$

$$f(x) = 2^x \qquad\qquad\qquad f(x) = \sqrt{5 - x^2}$$

11*52.   On the Resource Page provided by your teacher, find a box for each of the relations listed in problem 11*51. As you listen to the presentations, take notes on each relation. Be sure to sketch a graph of the relation as well as list any special points or features. Remember to date this entry and place the Resource Page with your Learning Reflections.

11*53.   MATCH-A-GRAPH

Match each rule (a) through (f) with its corresponding graph below.

a. $f(x) = \sqrt{x-3}$

b. $f(x) = \frac{1}{x}+1$

c. $f(x) = x^3 - 2$

d. $f(x) = \sqrt{5-(x+2)^2}$

e. $f(x) = \frac{3}{x^2}$

f. $f(x) = 2^{x-2}$

1)
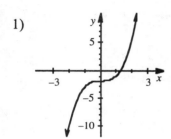

2)
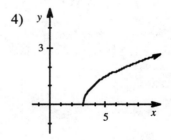

3)
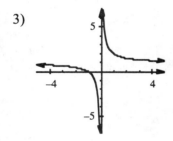

4)
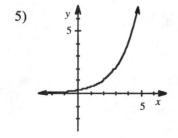

5)

6)
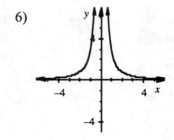

11*54. For each relation graphed in problem 11*53, name the domain and the range.

11*55. On the same set of axes, graph $y = |x|$ and $y = |x| + 2$. What is the same about these two graphs? What is different?

11*56. Solve each inequality for x.

a. $|x| - 4 > 1$

b. $|x - 4| > 1$

c. Compare parts (a) and (b) and their solutions. What do you notice? Is there any **connection**?

11*57. Find the corresponding inputs or outputs for the following relations. If there is no solution, explain why not. Be careful: In some cases, there may be no solution or more than one solution.

a. $x = 8$

$f(x) = |x|$

$f(8) = ?$

b. $x = ?$

$f(x) = 3 - \sqrt{x}$

$f(x) = 2$

c. $k = -6$

$f(k) = \frac{k}{2} + 1$

$f(-6) = ?$

c. $x = 3$

$f(x) = \sqrt{x - 5}$

$f(3) = ?$

11*58. Find the equation of a line that is perpendicular to $y = \frac{-1}{5}x + 11$ but goes through the point (6, 8).

11*59. Find the inputs for the following relations with the given outputs. If there is no possible input for the given output, explain why not.

a. $x = ?$

$f(x) = 3x - 7$

$f(x) = -1$

b. $x = ?$

$f(x) = \sqrt{2x - 6}$

$f(x) = 10$

11*60.   Simplify using only positive exponents.

a. $(3x^2y)(5x)$

b. $(x^2y^3)(x^{-2}y^{-2})$

c. $\frac{x^3}{x^{-2}}$

d. $(2x^{-1})^3$

11*61.   Solve each equation below for the given variable. Be sure to check your solution.

a. $6x - 11 = 3x + 16$

b. $-2(5 - 3x) + 5 = 9 + 3x$

c. $\frac{6}{k-2} = 10$

d. $\frac{4}{3x-1} = \frac{2}{x+3}$

11*62.   Find the point of intersection of the two lines below using any method.

$$7x - 3y = 2$$
$$y = 3x - 2$$

11*63.   Which graphs below have a domain of all numbers? Which have a range of all numbers?

a.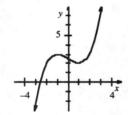

b.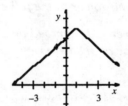

c.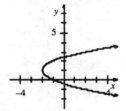

11*64.   Solve each of the following equations or systems.

a. $x^2 - 1 = 15$

b. $y = 3x - 2$
       $y = 4x + 3$

c. $x^2 - 2x - 8 = 0$

d. $2x^2 = -x + 7$

11*65.   Graph and shade the solution for the system of inequalities below.

$$y \le 4 + \tfrac{3}{4}x$$
$$y > -\tfrac{1}{2}x + 1$$

11.1.6 How does it change?

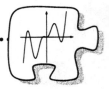

• •

Transformation of a Function

11*66.   PROMOTION OPPORTUNITY

You and your co-workers at Functions of
America have received the following note
from your boss. Read the letter and complete
the task that follows.

To My Faithful Employees,

*I have been pleased to read in the Relations
Daily about the high customer service
satisfaction ratings of this company. Now I
want to expand to control the function **rental**
industry. Before Functions of America can
begin renting out our expensive graphs, I would like an equation attached to each one.
That way, when a graph is returned to the company, employees will be able to verify
that it is the same function that was originally rented to the customer. Also, if the graph
of the function was damaged or switched for a less sophisticated graph, we will then be
able to prosecute the customer to the full extent of the law.*

*Employees will be given a designated time to explore their new and innovative function
with a partner. Please be ready to report on how the numbers in a rule change its
graph.*

*At the end of the day, every employee will be challenged to identify the equation of a
function correctly by observing only its graph. Doing so will earn you a management
position. I wish all of you the best of luck.*

> *Sincerely,*
> *Freda Function, CEO, F of A*

Your Task: Your teacher will assign your team one of the functions below. Explore
the graph of your function as a, h, and k change values. Choose positive, negative,
and zero values for a, h, and k to uncover all possible patterns. Reflect on the
relationships you find between the graph and its equation. Discuss your observations
with your study team and record your results on paper.

$$f(x) = a\sqrt{x-h} + k \qquad\qquad f(x) = a(x-h)^2 + k \qquad\qquad f(x) = a(x-h)^3 + k$$

$$f(x) = a|x-h| + k \qquad\qquad f(x) = \frac{a}{x-h} + k \qquad\qquad f(x) = 2^{(x-h)} + k$$

Discussion Points

What is the goal of this investigation?

What is the best way to choose values of a, h, and k to see a pattern?

Further Guidance

11*67.   When you asked for clarification, your boss sent you the following note:

Dear Employees,

Thanks for your questions. I am sorry I was so vague. In your report, I would like you to tell me:

1. *How does the equation affect how "skinny" or "wide" the graph is?*
2. *What changes in the equation move the graph up or down? Left or right?*
3. *Is there a way to change the equation so that the function turns "upside down"?*

Use your graphing technology to test different values of a, h, and k to discover the answers to the questions above. Examine only one letter at a time so that you can find patterns quickly. For example, if you want to see what the value of a does to the graph of a function, then change a while you keep h and k the same.

Good luck!
Ms. Function

11*68.   Start with the function you have been assigned.

a.   Choose values of a, h, and k and draw the graph accurately on graph paper.

b.   Give this graph to another pair of students and challenge them to find the equation of your graph.

c.   Find a graph from another team and determine its equation using the patterns and observations from your work in problems 11*66 or 11*67.

d.   Repeat this activity as often as time permits.

11*69.   PROMOTION CHALLENGE

Here is your opportunity to impress your boss. Find the equation for each relation graphed below. Remember the observations you made in problem 11*66 and pay close attention to details.

a.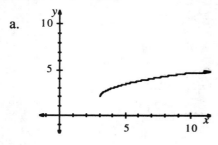

b.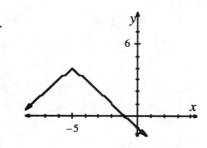

11*70. EXTENSION

How do the domain and range of a function change when it moves? To answer this question, examine what happens as the square root function below is moved ("translated").

a. Describe the domain and range of $f(x) = \sqrt{x}$.

b. Now describe the domain and range of $g(x) = \sqrt{x+2} - 3$.

c. Are the domain and range for $f(x)$ and $g(x)$ above the same? If not, how are they different?

Review & Preview

11*71. Match each rule below with its corresponding graph. Can you do this without making any tables?

a. $y = |x-1|$ b. $y = |x| + 3$ c. $y = |x-1| + 3$

1) 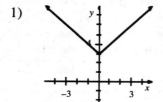   2) 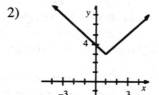   3)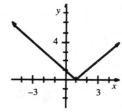

11*72. Graph the rule $y = -x^2 + 4x$ and label its intercepts and vertex.

11*73. If $f(x) = 7 + |x|$ and $g(x) = x^3 - 5$, then find:

a. $f(-5)$ b. $g(4)$ c. $f(0)$ d. $f(2)$

e. $g(-2)$ f. $g(0)$

11*74. Solve for x in each equation below.

a. $2x = 8$ b. $2x + 2 = 10$

c. $6x + 2 - 4x = 10$ d. $2(3x+1) - 4x = 10$

e. Check your solutions for the equations above. What do you notice?

11*75. Multiply each expression below using generic rectangles.

a. $(4x-1)(3x+2)$ b. $(m+1)(3m-2)$ c. $(k-4)(6-5k)$

11*76. Solve the following inequalities for x. Graph your solutions on a number line.

a. $3x - 5 \le 7 + 2x$ b. $|x| - 3 < 7$

c. $5(2-x) + 6 > 16$ d. $|x+2| > 3$

11.2.1 Intercept or intersect?

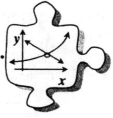

Intercepts and Intersections

Now that you know about many kinds of functions, you will look more closely at intercepts and intersections. What is the difference between an intercept and a point of intersection? Think about this as you develop algebraic methods to find points where two functions cross. In the next few lessons you will have chances to practice your quadratic solving skills as well as your newer solving skills from Chapter 10.

11*77.   Examine the graphs of the parabola $y = x^2 - 3x - 10$
and line $y = -2x + 2$ at right.

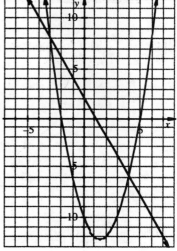

a.   Name all x- and y-intercepts for the parabola.

b.   Name all x- and y-intercepts for the line.

c.   Where do the graphs intersect each other?

d.   The words "intersect" and "intercept" look and
sound a lot alike, but what do they mean? How
are they alike? How are they different?

11*78.   Intercepts and intersections are similar, but they are not exactly the same. How can you
tell which one you are looking for? Read the situations below and decide if the
graphical solution would best be represented as an **intercept** or an **intersection**. Be
prepared to defend your decision. Note: You do not need to solve the problem!

a.   A 5-gram candle on a birthday cake is lit. Two minutes after it is lit,
the candle weighs 4.2 grams. How long will the candle burn?

b.   A local bowling alley charges you $4 to rent shoes and $3.50 for each game you
play. Another alley charges you $7 to rent shoes and $2 for each game you play.
How many games would you need to play in order for both alleys to charge you
the same amount?

c.   Two months after Aliya's birthday, she had $450, while her sister
Claudia had $630. Five months after her birthday, Aliya had $800,
while Claudia had $920. How much did each person have on
Aliya's birthday?

11*79.   Using a graph to find the intersection of two curves can be challenging when the rules are complicated or when the point of intersection ends up off the graph. Therefore, it helps to know another way to find the intersection without using a graph.

   a.   Name the algebraic methods you already know to solve linear systems.

   b.   Use one of the methods you listed in part (a) to solve for the intersection of $y = x^2 - 3x - 10$ and $y = -2x + 2$. Be sure to collaborate with your teammates and check your results along the way. Does the graph in problem 11*77 confirm your results?

11*80.   Solve the system of equations below for x and y. Write your solution(s) in the form (x, y). Then graph the system on the same set of axes and confirm your solution.
$$y = \frac{1}{x^2}$$
$$y = \frac{1}{3x+10}$$

11*81.   In your Learning Reflection, explain the difference between intercepts and intersections. Include a sketch or graph to help your explanation. Title this entry "Intercepts and Intersections" and include today's date.

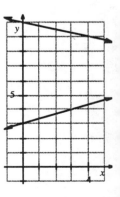

Review & Preview

11*82.   Find the output for the following relation with the given input. If there is no possible output for the given input, explain why not.

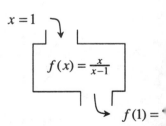
$x = 1$
$f(x) = \frac{x}{x-1}$
$f(1) =$

11*83.   Examine the two lines graphed at right. Will these two lines intersect? Find the equation of each line and test your prediction.

11*84.   For each line in problem 11*83, find the x- and y-intercepts.

11*85.   Which of the equations below is equivalent to $4(3x-1)+3x=9x+5$? More than one may be equivalent. **Justify** your answer.

a. $12x-4+3x=9x+5$ b. $12x-1+3x=9x+5$

c. $11x=14x$ d. $15x-4=9x+5$

11*86.   Paula graphed a line and found that $f(-2)=5$ and $f(0)=2$. Graph this line and find its equation.

11*87.   Which of the relations below are functions? **Justify** your answer.

a.    b. 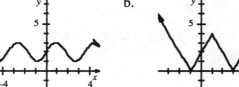   c.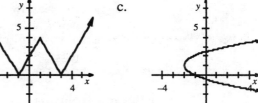

11*88.   For each graph in problem 11*87 above, name the domain and range.

11*89.   Examine the graphs in problem 11*87 again. Which, if any, have symmetry? Copy each graph on your paper and show any lines of symmetry.

11.2.2 How many points of intersection?

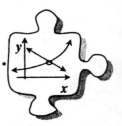

Pulling It All Together

In Lesson 9.4.1, you developed a method for finding the points of intersection of a line and a parabola. Today you will study different possibilities for lines and parabolas intersecting or not intersecting.

11*90.   As you have seen, sometimes a parabola and a line never intersect. However, if a parabola and a line do intersect, how many different intersection points can they have? How many intersections can two parabolas have? Do two parabolas **always** intersect?

On graph paper, sketch a graph that fits each description below. Not every graph is possible. As you graph, consider the questions above.

a.   A line and a parabola that intersect twice.

b.   A line and a parabola that intersect once.

c.   A line and a parabola that intersect more than twice.

d.   Two parabolas that intersect twice.

e.   Two parabolas that have an infinite number of intersections.

f.   Two parabolas that never intersect.

g.   Two parabolas that only intersect once.

11*91.   INTERSECTION POSTER ACTIVITY

When given a graph of two parabolas or a line and a parabola, it is usually easy to determine how many points of intersection they have. However, how can you tell algebraically?

Your Task: Each team will be assigned one of the systems below. With your team:

•   Use any algebraic solving method to find the point(s) of intersection for your team's system, if any exist. Examine your algebraic solution and decide what it indicates about the graph of the system. (That is, do the parabolas intersect once? Do they not intersect?)

•   Once you have solved your team's system, have your teacher come to your team and listen to you explain your results. Use a graphing calculator (or sketch a graph using your graphing shortcuts) to verify your conclusion.

Continued on next page →

11*91.   *Continued from previous page*

- Design a poster that shows the algebraic solution of your system as well as a sketch of the graph.

Systems:

a. $y = x^2$
    $y = 2x - 1$

b. $y = x^2 - 5x + 6$
    $y = -x^2$

c. $y = x^2 - 4x + 5$
    $y = -x^2 + 4x - 1$

d. $y = x^2 - x - 2$
    $y = x^2 + 2x + 1$

e. $y = x^2 - x - 2$
    $y = x - 6$

f. $y = 2x^2 + 3x - 9$
    $y = x - 5$

11*92.   ALGEBRA COMES TO THE RESCUE!

Darrel is so excited! When he called his local radio station during a contest, he was the 9th caller! The talk show host, Maribel, explained that Darrel would win a brand new graphing calculator if he answers this question correctly: *"How many times do the parabola* $y = 2x^2 - 5x$ *and the line* $y = \frac{2}{3}x - 4$ *intersect?"*

a.   Quickly, Darrel used his graphing calculator to graph the system—but then his calculator broke! Help him by graphing the system on your grapher. Time is running out... what should he tell Maribel?

b.   Maribel paused and then asked, *"Are you **absolutely sure** that is your final answer?"* Help Darrel confirm his answer by solving the system algebraically. What is the correct answer?

11*93.   Solve each quadratic equation below using any method you choose. Check your solutions.

   a. $(5x - 1)(x + 3) = 0$ b. $4x^2 + 10x - 6 = 0$

   c. $0.5x^2 - 3x + 4.5 = 0$ d. $x^2 + 5x = 14$

11*94.   Use your graphing shortcuts to graph $f(x) = x^2 - 6x + 5$.

   a.   What is the vertex?

   b.   Describe the domain and range of this relation.

11*95.   Solve the following problem with a Guess and Check table. Write your solution as a sentence.

   Mr. Ripley's fruit stand sells watermelons for $5 and apples for $2. Last weekend, he sold 40 pieces of fruit (all apples and watermelons) for $107. How many watermelons did he sell?

11*96.   Find all points where the graphs of $y = x^2 - 3x + 2$ and $y = 2x + 8$ intersect.

11*97.   **Multiple Choice:** Which of the lines below is parallel to the line $5x - 3y = 11$?

   a. $5x - 3y = 4$ b. $5x + 3y = -2$ c. $3x - 5y = 11$ d. $3x + 5y = -1$

11*98.   **Multiple Choice:** Which expression below is a factor of $4x^2 + 8x - 5$?

   a. $2x - 5$ b. $2x - 1$ c. $2x + 1$ d. $x + 5$

11.2.3 Where do functions intersect?

Intersecting Functions

Now that you have an understanding of points of intersections as well as the skills you need to solve a wide variety of equations, you will put all these pieces together. You will find points of intersection for systems of interesting non-linear functions. As you work today, use the following questions to guide your team's discussion.

How can we tell where the functions will cross?

How can we solve the system?

How can we check our solutions?

11*99. Your teacher will assign your team one of the following systems of functions.

i.
$$f(x) = x^2 + 1$$
$$g(x) = |2x|$$

ii.
$$f(x) = \sqrt{4 - x}$$
$$g(x) = \tfrac{-1}{3} x + 2$$

iii.
$$f(x) = \tfrac{x^2}{x-1}$$
$$g(x) = \tfrac{3}{2} x$$

iv.
$$f(x) = x^3 - 2x$$
$$f(x) = x^2$$

v.
$$f(x) = \tfrac{1-x}{x}$$
$$g(x) = \tfrac{-3}{x+4}$$

a. Analyze your system by using algebra to find the following:

- all x- and y-intercepts

- all points of intersection

b. Confirm your results by carefully graphing your system on graph paper.

11*100. Prepare a presentation to share your results with the class. Create a poster or overhead transparency that shows both your algebraic solution and your graphical solution to your system.

11*101. In a Learning Reflection, describe how you can use algebra to find the point(s) of intersection of two functions. Be sure to include an example. Title this reflection "Finding Intersections of Functions" and label it with today's date.

11*102.　Solve the following equation and inequality.

　　　　a.　　$(x-5)^2 = 2x^2 + 3x - 4$ 　　　　　　　b.　　$|2x^2 - 5| \le 3$

11*103.　Find all of the points where the functions at right intersect.　　$f(x) = \frac{1}{x+2}$
　　　　　　　　　　　　　　　　　　　　　　　　　　　　　　　　$g(x) = x - 3$

11*104.　Graph $f(x) = |2x^2 - 3|$. Find the domain and range.

11*105.　Graph the solution to the system of inequalities at right.　　$y \ge x^2 + 3$
　　　　　　　　　　　　　　　　　　　　　　　　　　　　　　　$y < -x^2 + 1$

11*106.　Simplify each of the following expressions. Assume the denominators do not equal zero.

　　　　a.　　$\frac{x^9 y z^2}{x^5 y^{-1} z^{-2}}$　　　　　　b.　　$\frac{3x^2 - 5x - 28}{5x^2 - 18x - 8}$　　　　　　c.　　$\frac{x^4 - 4x^3 - 5x^2}{x^3 + 7x^2 + 6x}$

11.3.1 Can we find it?

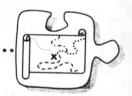

Relation Treasure Hunt

Now that we have many ways to describe a relation, we can use these ways to distinguish between different relations that are given in different representations.

11*107.　RELATION TREASURE HUNT

Today you will be given several descriptive clues about different relations. For each clue, work with a partner to find possible matches among the relations posted around the classroom. Remember that more than one relation may match each clue. Once you have decided which relation(s) match a given clue, defend your decision to your teacher and receive the next clue. Be sure to record your matches on paper.

Your goal is to find the match(es) for each of **eight** clues. Once you and your partner have finished, only one relation will be left unmatched. That relation is the treasure!

11*108.   For each relation graphed below, describe the domain (input) and range (output).

a.

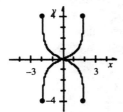

b.

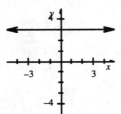

c.

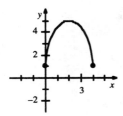

d.

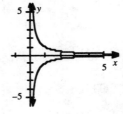

11*109.   For each relation graphed in problem 11*108, explain whether it is a function. If the relation is not a function, give a reason to support your claim.

11*110.   What number is not part of the domain of $f(x) = \frac{3}{x+5}$? How can you tell?

11*111.   Find the equation of the line perpendicular to $5x - 2y = 13$ that passes through the point (60, –20).

11*112.   Use fraction busters to solve for x: $\frac{4}{3x} + \frac{6}{x} = 9$.

11*113.   Find all of the points at which the parabolas below intersect. Write your solution(s) in (x, y) form.

$$y = x^2 + 5x - 4$$
$$y = x^2 + x - 12$$

① TEAM BRAINSTORM

With your team, brainstorm a list for each of the following topics. Be as detailed as you can. How long can you make your list? Challenge yourselves.

Topics: What have we studied in this chapter? What ideas and words were important in what we learned? Remember to be as detailed as you can.

Ways of Thinking: What ways of thinking have we used in this chapter? When did we use them?

Connections: What topics, ideas, and words that we learned *before* this chapter are connected to the new ideas in this chapter? Again, make your list as long as you can.

Be prepared to share your team's ideas with the class.

② MAKING CONNECTIONS

The following is a list of all of the key words in this chapter. The words that appear in bold are new to this chapter. Make sure that you are familiar with all of these words.

domain (p. 474)	equation	**function (p. 469, 474)**
graph	input	intersection
output	**range (p. 474)**	**relation (p. 474)**
solution	*x*-intercept	*x*→*y* table
y-intercept		

Make a concept map showing all of the **connections** you can find between the key words and ideas listed above. For each key word or idea, sketch an example. Label each connection with a phrase explaining how the ideas are related. While you are making your map, you may think of related ideas that are not listed above. Be sure to include these ideas in your concept map.

③ SUMMARIZING MY UNDERSTANDING

This section gives you an opportunity to show what you know about one or more topics or ideas. Your teacher will give you directions for exactly how to do this.

④ WHERE AM I?

This section will help you evaluate which types of problems you have seen that you feel comfortable with and which ones you need more help with. This section appears at the end of every chapter to help you check your understanding. Even if your teacher does not assign this section, it is a good idea to try the problems and find out for yourself what you know and what you need to work on.

Solve each problem as completely as you can. The table at the end of the closure section has answers to these problems. It also tells you where you can find additional help and practice on problems like these.

CL 11*1. For each of the representations below, decide if the relation represented is a function. **Justify** your answer.

a.

x	y
4	8
7	8
45	7
52	-6
7	9
13	0

b.

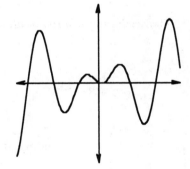

c.

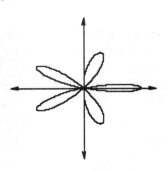

d. $2x + 3y = 4$

CL 11*2. Examine the relation $h(x)$ defined at right. Then estimate the values below.

a. $h(1)$

b. $h(3)$

c. x when $h(x) = 0$

d. $h(-1)$

e. $h(-4)$

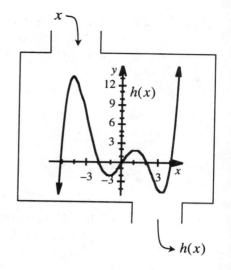

CL 11*3. Consider the parabola $y = 2x^2 + 6x - 20$.

a. Find this parabola's x- and y-intercepts.

b. Find where this parabola intersects the x-axis.

c. Find where the parabola intersects the line $y = 3x + 1$.

CL 11*4. Solve for the given variable.

a. $|2m - 7| = 16$

b. $\sqrt{3y + 8} = 5$

c. $(-x + 8)^2 \geq 16$

d. $12 > |3x + 15|$

CL 11*5. For each system of equations, find both coordinates of the point(s) of intersection.

a. $2x + 3y = 7$
$-3x - 5y = -13$

b. $y = 2x^2 - 12x + 18$
$y = x^2 + 4x - 10$

c. $y = x - 1$
$y = \frac{2}{x}$

d. $y = 2x - 4.5$
$18 = 8x - 4y$

CL 11*6. Simplify the expressions below. Your answers should have no parentheses or negative exponents. Assume the denominators do not equal zero.

a. $\dfrac{(x + 3)^4}{3x^2 - 11x - 70} \div \dfrac{x^2 + 6x + 9}{x - 7}$

b. $\dfrac{24a^{12}b^0c^{-3} \cdot 2^2 a^{-3}c^{-2}}{(6a^4b^3)^2}$

CL 11*7. Check your answers to each problem above using the table at the end of the closure section. Which problems did you feel confident about? Which problems were hard? Use the table to make a list of topics you need help on and a list of topics you need to practice more.

⑤ HOW AM I THINKING?

This course emphasizes the following five Ways of Thinking:

- Reversing processes (going in both directions)
- Justifying (explaining why)
- Generalizing (showing how it works for all cases)
- Making Connections (showing how it fits in with other ideas)
- Applying and/or extending our knowledge (thinking about how we use it or where it can go)

Choose three of these Ways of Thinking that you remember using while working in this chapter. For each way of thinking that you choose, show and explain where you used it and how you used it. Describe why thinking in this way helped you solve a particular problem or understand something new. (For instance, explain why we wanted to generalize in this particular case, or why it was useful to see these particular connections.) Be sure to include examples to demonstrate your thinking.

Problem	Solution	Need Help?	More Practice
CL 11*1.	a. no b. yes c. no d. yes	Sections 11.1.3 and 11.1.4, MN p. 474	11*38(d), 11*40(a), 11*45, 11*87, 11*109
CL 11*2.	a. 2 b. –4 c. –5, –2, 0, 2, 4 d. –2 e. 6	Section 11.1.2, MN p, 474	11*17, 11*20, 11*38
CL 11*3.	a. x-intercepts $(2, 0)$ and $(–5, 0)$, y-intercept $(0, –20)$ b. $(–5, 0)$ and $(–2, 0)$ c. approximately $(2.6, 8.8)$ and $(–4.1, –11.2)$	Sections 11.2.1 and 11.2.2	11*14, 11*72, 11*77, 11*79(b), 11*80, 11*96
CL 11*4.	a. $m = \frac{23}{2}$, $-\frac{9}{2}$ b. $y = \frac{17}{3}$ c. $x \le 4$ or $x \ge 12$ d. $-9 < x < -1$	MN p. 440, Sections 10.2.4 and 10.2.5	11*10, 11*35, 11*56, 11*76, 11*102(b)
CL 11*5.	a. $(–4, 5)$ b. $(2, 2)$ and $(14, 242)$ c. $(2, 1)$ and $(–1, –2)$ d. $(-\frac{9}{8}, -\frac{27}{4}) = (–1.125, –6.75)$	Sections 11.2.1 and 11.2.3	11*62, 11*79, 11*80, 11*96, 11*99, 11*103, 11*113
CL 11*6.	a. $\frac{(x+3)^2}{3x+10}$ b. $\frac{8a}{3b^6c^5}$	MN p. 410, MN p. 424, Section 10.1.6	11*13, 11*15, 11*50, 11*106

CHAPTER 12 Algebraic Extensions

As the title of this final chapter suggests, you will revisit and build upon many of the topics you have studied so far in this course. For example, you already have learned how to simplify, multiply, and divide rational expressions. In this chapter, you will develop a method to add and subtract them.

In addition, you will revisit quadratics and will apply your techniques of problem solving to solve new kinds of word problems.

Finally, you will pull together the knowledge and tools you have gained throughout this course to solve a series of exciting and challenging problems.

In this chapter, you will learn:

> How to add and subtract rational expressions.

> How to factor a difference of squares or a perfect square trinomial quickly without using a generic rectangle.

> How to solve word problems involving work and mixtures.

> How to derive the Quadratic Formula by completing the square.

> How to provide thorough mathematical justification for predictions and solutions.

Guiding Questions

Think about these questions throughout this chapter:

How can I rewrite it?

What's the connection?

Is there a shortcut?

Chapter Outline

Section 12.1 You will expand your ability to rewrite expressions by learning new ways to factor special quadratics and to add and subtract rational expressions.

Section 12.2 You will learn how to solve word problems about making mixtures and working together.

Section 12.3 You will learn how to derive the Quadratic Formula.

Section 12.4 You will apply the mathematics you have learned throughout this course to analyze a challenging pattern, make a prediction about a burning candle, analyze an interesting inequality, and find the maximum area of a pen for a cow.

12.1.1 Is there a shortcut?

Are there any types of quadratics that you can factor quickly without using a generic rectangle? If so, what do these quadratics look like and how can we recognize them? Today your team will examine the factored forms of many different quadratics and look for patterns and shortcuts for factoring certain types of quadratics.

12*1.   SPECIAL QUADRATICS

Your team will be assigned several of the quadratics below to factor (if possible). Look for similarities and differences among the problems and solutions. Be prepared to share your solution with the class. Then work as a class to put the quadratics into groups based on the patterns you find in their factored forms.

a. $x^2 - 49$

b. $x^2 + 2x - 24$

c. $x^2 - 10x + 25$

d. $9x^2 + 12x + 4$

e. $5x^2 - 4x - 1$

f. $4x^2 - 25$

g. $x^2 - 6x + 9$

h. $x^2 - 36$

i. $7x^2 - 20x - 3$

j. $4x^2 + 20x + 25$

k. $x^2 + 4$

l. $9x^2 - 1$

12*2.   Which of the following quadratics fit the patterns you found in problem 12*1? Factor each of the following expressions using your new shortcuts, if possible.

a. $25x^2 - 1$

b. $x^2 - 5x - 36$

c. $x^2 + 8x + 16$

d. $9x^2 - 12x + 4$

e. $9x^2 + 4$

f. $9x^2 - 100$

12*3.   Special quadratics, like $9x^2 - 100$ in part (f) above, can be factored quickly once you learn the pattern. But why do the patterns you found in problem 12*1 work?

   a.   Quadratics in the form $a^2x^2 - b^2$ are called **difference of squares**. Use a generic rectangle to prove that $a^2x^2 - b^2 = (ax - b)(ax + b)$. Be ready to share your work with the class.

   b.   Quadratics in the form $a^2x^2 + 2abx + b^2$ are called **perfect square trinomials**. Use a generic rectangle to prove that $a^2x^2 + 2abx + b^2 = (ax + b)^2$. Be ready to share your work with the class.

12*4.   As a Learning Reflection, describe how to factor a difference of squares and a perfect square trinomial. Be sure to include an example of each type. Title this entry "Factoring Shortcuts" and include today's date.

Review & Preview

12*5.   Use your factoring shortcuts to simplify the following expressions. Assume the denominators do not equal zero.

   a. $\dfrac{x^2-9}{x^2-6x+9}$

   b. $\dfrac{2x+5}{4x^2-25} \cdot \dfrac{2x-5}{x+7}$

   c. $\dfrac{x^2+x-20}{x^2-16} \cdot \dfrac{x^2+9x+20}{x^2+10x+25}$

   d. $\dfrac{x^2+12x+36}{x^2-25} \div \dfrac{x+6}{x+5}$

12*6.   Solve the following equations for x.

   a. $4x - 6y = 20$

   b. $\tfrac{1}{2}x - 6 = 9$

   c. $2(4 - x) + 5x = 3(x + 9)$

   d. $-x - y = -1$

*7. Simplify each expression below. Your answer should contain no parentheses and no negative exponents.

a. $(-\frac{2}{3}x^5 y^{1/3})^0$

b. $(25^{1/2} x^5)(4x^{-6})$

c. $5t^{-1/2}$

d. $\dfrac{8^{1/3} x^4 y}{4x^{3/2} y^3}$

*8. Examine the graphs of relations $f(x)$ and $g(x)$ at right. Use the graph to approximate the values below (if possible).

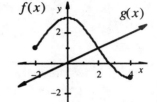

a. $f(0)$

b. $g(4)$

c. $f(-3)$

d. $g(0)$

e. $g(2)$

f. $f(2)$

*9. Solve the equations and inequalities below by first completing the square.

a. $x^2 - 2x - 3 \le 0$

b. $x^2 + 4x = 3$

c. $x^2 + 12x + 39 > 0$

d. $x^2 - 3x - 13.75 = 0$

*10. Describe how you add and subtract fractions that have a common denominator.

a. Add or subtract the fractions below. Draw a diagram to show that your answer is correct.

i. $\frac{8}{11} - \frac{3}{11}$

ii. $\frac{x}{6} + \frac{2}{6}$

b. As you know, fractions you need to add or subtract do not always have the same denominator. What if you are given two fractions to add or subtract and the denominators are not the same? Add the fractions below and check your result on your calculator.

$$\frac{1}{3} + \frac{2}{5}$$

*11. Examine the graph of the relation at right.

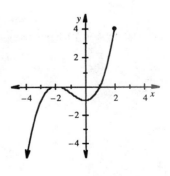

a. Use inequalities to name its domain and range.

b. Is this relation a function? How can you tell?

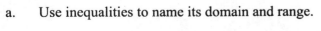

12.1.2 How can I rewrite it?

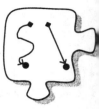

So far in this course you have learned a lot about rational expressions. You have learned how to simplify complex algebraic fractions by factoring the numerators and denominators. You have also learned how to multiply and divide rational expressions. What else can we learn? Today y will develop a method to add and subtract algebraic fractions.

12*12. With your team, review your responses to homework problem 12*10. Verify that everyone obtained the same answers and be prepared to share how you added fractio with the class.

$$\frac{8}{11} - \frac{3}{11} \qquad\qquad \frac{x}{6} + \frac{2}{6} \qquad\qquad \frac{1}{3} + \frac{2}{5}$$

12*13. Use your understanding of adding fractions to add the algebraic expressions below. Then simplify your solution, if possible. Assume the denominators do not equal zero

a. $\dfrac{2x}{2x^2+x-21} + \dfrac{7}{2x^2+x-21}$

b. $\dfrac{5x}{x^2-2x-3} - \dfrac{15}{x^2-2x-3}$

c. $\dfrac{3x+9}{8x^2-50} - \dfrac{x+4}{8x^2-50}$

d. $\dfrac{x^2+5x-2}{3x^2+2x-8} + \dfrac{2x^2-3x-6}{3x^2+2x-8}$

12*14. What if the algebraic fractions do not have the same denominator? With your team, discuss how to add the fractions below. Be prepared to **justify** your strategy with the class. Assume the denominators do not equal zero.

a. $\dfrac{x}{3x+1} + \dfrac{2x^2-2}{(x-5)(3x+1)}$

b. $\dfrac{9-3x}{(x+3)(x-3)} + \dfrac{2x}{x+3}$

12*15. As a Learning Reflection, explain how to add and subtract rational expressions. Be sure to include an example. Title this entry "Adding and Subtracting Rational Expressions" and include today's date.

2*16. Use your understanding of adding fractions to add the algebraic expressions below. Then simplify your solution, if possible.

    a. $\dfrac{5m+18}{m+3} + \dfrac{4m+9}{m+3}$ b. $\dfrac{3a^2+a-1}{a^2-2a+1} - \dfrac{2a^2-a+2}{a^2-2a+1}$

2*17. Solve the equations and inequalities below. Check your solution(s), if possible.

    a. $|5x+8| \geq -4$ b. $x^2+x-20 < 0$

    c. $2x^2-6x = -5$ d. $\frac{5}{9} - \frac{x}{3} = \frac{4}{9}$

2*18. **Multiple Choice:** Which of the following expressions is equivalent to $x^2-12x+40$?

    a. $(x-6)^2+4$ b. $(x-6)^2+28$ c. $(x-12)^2+4$ d. $(x-12)^2$

2*19. Multiply the following expressions using generic rectangles.

    a. $(5m-1)(m+2)$ b. $(6-x)(2+x)$

    c. $2x(3y+5x)$ d. $3x(2x-5y+4)$

2*20. Examine the graphs of each relation below. Decide if each is a function or not. Then describe the domain and range of each.

    a. 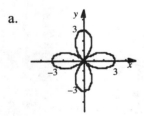   b.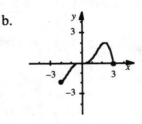

2*21. Graph the function $g(x) = \frac{x+2}{x-1}$ on graph paper and name all x- and y-intercepts. What happens at $x = 1$?

2*22. If $f(x) = 3x-9$ and $g(x) = -x^2$, find:

    a. $f(-2)$ b. $g(-2)$ c. x if $f(x) = 0$ d. $g(m)$

12.1.3 How can I rewrite it?

Today you will complete your work with rational expressions. By the end of this lesson you wil
know how to add, subtract, multiply, and divide rational expressions.

12*23. Review what you learned in Lesson 12.1.2 by adding and subtracting the expressions
below. Leave your solution as simplified as possible. Assume the denominators do r
equal zero.

a. $\frac{5}{8} + \frac{1}{6}$

b. $\frac{8}{9} - \frac{2}{3}$

c. $\frac{x+5}{x+2} + \frac{2x+1}{x+2}$

d. $\frac{x^2-3}{(x+5)(2x-1)} + \frac{x}{2x-1}$

12*24. Examine the expression below.

$$\frac{2x-1}{3x^2+13x+4} + \frac{x+3}{x^2-3x-28}$$

a. With your team, decide how you can alter the expression so that the fractions h
a common denominator. Be ready to share your idea with the class.

b. Add the fractions and simplify the result, if possible.

c. Repeat the process to subtract $\frac{2}{x+4} - \frac{4x-x^2}{x^2-16}$. Simplify the result, if possible.

12*25. **PULLING IT ALL TOGETHER**

You now know how to add, subtract, multiply, and divide rational expressions. Pull
this all together by simplifying the following expressions.

a. $\frac{x^2-3x-10}{x^2-4x-5} \div \frac{x^2-7x-18}{2x^2-5x-7}$

b. $\frac{2x^2+x}{(2x+1)^2} - \frac{3}{2x+1}$

c. $\frac{15x-20}{x-5} \cdot \frac{x^2-2x-15}{3x^2+5x-12}$

d. $\frac{4}{2x+3} + \frac{x^2-x-2}{2x^2+5x+3}$

e. $\frac{6x-4}{3x^2-17x+10} - \frac{1}{x^2-2x-15}$

f. $\frac{x^2-x-2}{4x^2-7x-2} \div \frac{x^2-2x-3}{3x^2-8x-3}$

MATH NOTES

Adding and Subtracting Rational Expressions

The Least Common Multiple of $(x + 3)(x + 2)$ and $x + 2$ is $(x + 3)(x + 2)$.

$$\frac{4}{(x+2)(x+3)} + \frac{2x}{x+2}$$

The denominator of the first fraction already is the Least Common Multiple. To get a common denominator in the **second** fraction, multiply the fraction by $\frac{(x+3)}{(x+3)}$, a form of one (1).

$$= \frac{4}{(x+2)(x+3)} + \frac{2x}{x+2}\left[\frac{(x+3)}{(x+3)}\right]$$

Multiply the numerator and denominator of the second term.

$$= \frac{4}{(x+2)(x+3)} + \frac{2x(x+3)}{(x+2)(x+3)}$$

Distribute the numerator.

$$= \frac{4}{(x+2)(x+3)} + \frac{2x^2+6x}{(x+2)(x+3)}$$

Add, factor, and simplify.

$$= \frac{2x^2+6x+4}{(x+2)(x+3)} = \frac{2(x+1)(x+2)}{(x+2)(x+3)} = \frac{2(x+1)}{(x+3)}$$

Review & Preview

2*26.   Add, subtract, multiply, or divide the following rational expressions. Simplify your answer if possible. Assume the denominators do not equal zero.

a. $\dfrac{2x}{3x^2+16x+5} + \dfrac{10}{3x^2+16x+5}$

b. $\dfrac{x^2-x-12}{3x^2-11x-4} \cdot \dfrac{3x^2-20x-7}{x^2-9}$

c. $\dfrac{2x^2+8x-10}{2x^2+15x+25} \div \dfrac{4x^2+20x-24}{2x^2+x-10}$

d. $\dfrac{16x-12}{4x^2+5x-6} - \dfrac{3}{x+2}$

2*27.   Examine the graph of $f(x) = |x - 3| + 1$ at right. Use the graph to find the values listed below.

a. $f(3)$ b. $f(0)$

c. $f(4)$ d. $f(-1)$

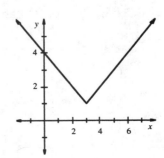

12*28. Use the graph of $f(x) = |x - 3| + 1$ in problem 12*27 to solve the equations and inequalities below. It may be helpful to copy the graph onto graph paper first.

a. $|x - 3| + 1 = 1$

b. $|x - 3| + 1 \leq 4$

c. $|x - 3| + 1 = 3$

d. $|x - 3| + 1 > 2$

12*29. Solve the quadratic below **twice**: once by factoring and using the Zero Product Prope and once by completing the square. Verify that the solutions match.

$$x^2 + 14x + 33 = 0$$

12*30. Match each graph below with its domain.

a. D: All numbers

b. D: All numbers more than –2

c. D: All numbers less than or equal to 3

1)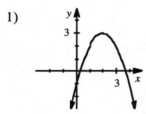

2)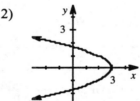

3)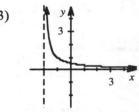

12*31. Graph the two functions below and find all points where they intersect. List all poin in the form (x, y).

$$f(x) = x^2 - 3x - 10$$

$$g(x) = -5x - 7$$

12*32. Rich has $1,268,714 and is spending $2,742 per day. Fred, on the other hand, has $231,384 and is saving $100 per day. When will they have the same amount of money saved?

12.2.1 How can we solve it?

So far in this course you have learned to solve many different types of word problems using a variety of tools. During Section 12.2, you will complete your understanding of solving word problems by focusing on two new types: those that involve work and those that involve mixture.

2*33.   MOWING THE LAWN

The National Mall, located in Washington D.C., is a mile-long rectangular lawn surrounded by several museums and famous monuments. It has been the site of many major historical and political events, such as the civil rights march of over 200,000 people, led by Martin Luther King Jr., on August 28, 1963.

Today the lawn is cared for by two teams of gardeners. It takes one team 10 hours to mow the lawn, while it takes the other team 15 hours.

Your Task: With your team, determine how long it would take to mow the entire lawn if both teams of gardeners work together. Create a diagram on graph paper to represent the work done by each team. Write and solve an equation for this situation. Be sure to define your variable(s).

Discussion Points

What is the goal of this task?

About how many hours would it take to mow the lawn if they worked together? Make an estimate. Is it more or less than 10 hours? Why?

Does it matter how big the lawn is?
Why or why not?

How much of the lawn does each team of gardeners mow in one hour?
How can you tell?

Further Guidance

12*34. To help solve problem 12*33, analyze what each piece of information gives you.

    a. One team of gardeners can mow the lawn in 10 hours. How much of the lawn this team mow in one hour? Draw a diagram to represent how much of the la this team can mow in one hour.

    b. The other team of gardeners can mow the lawn in 15 hours. How much of the lawn can this second team mow in one hour? Draw a diagram to represent ho much of the lawn this team can mow in one hour.

    c. Working together, how much of the lawn is mowed per hour? Explain how y got your answer.

    d. How long will it take for both teams of gardeners to mow the entire lawn? Explain how you got your answer.

    e. Write and solve an equation to represent this situation. Be sure to define your variables.

12*35. Hong can staple the programs for graduation in 30 minutes. However, since Eva ha electric stapler, it only takes her 10 minutes. If they work together, how long will it take to staple the programs? Be ready to share your work with the class.

12*36. It takes Frederick 8 minutes to wash his dad's truck. When he works with his sister, it takes them only 6 minutes together. How long would it take his sister to wash the truck alone? Write and solve an equation for this situation.

12*37. Ellie estimates that it would take 3 students 2 hours to hang 50 streamers for the pro If she has 5 students hang streamers for 3 hours, how many streamers can be hung? Explain how you found your answer.

12*38. Solve the quadratic equation below **twice**, once by first completing the square and once by using the Quadratic Formula. Leave all solutions in exact form. Verify that your solutions from each method match.

$$x^2 + 11 = 8x$$

12*39. Susan can paint her living room in 2 hours. Her friend, Jaime, estimates it would take him 3 hours to paint the same room. If they work together, how long will it take them to paint Susan's living room?

12*40. Write and solve an equation (or system of equations) for the situation below. Define your variable(s) and write your solution as a sentence.

Jessica has 147 coins that are all dimes and quarters. The number of quarters is 6 fewer than twice the number of dimes. If she has $29.10 in total, how many quarters does she have?

12*41. **Multiple Choice:** Which of the following expressions are equivalent to $12x^6$? (Note: More than one answer is possible.)

a. $3(2x^3)^2$ b. $(6x^8)(2x^{-2})$ c. $(144x^{12})^{1/2}$ d. $\dfrac{60x^{10}y}{5x^4 y}$

12*42. If $f(-1) = 7$ and $f(3) = 8$, and if the graph of $f(x)$ is a line:

a. Graph the line on graph paper.

b. Find the equation for $f(x)$.

12*43. The graph of the relation $f(x)$ is shown at right. Use the graph to estimate the following values.

a. $f(1)$ b. $f(-2)$

c. x if $f(x) = 0$ d. x if $f(x) = 3$

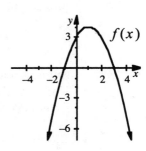

12*44. Find the equation of $f(x)$ graphed in problem 12*43.

12.2.2 How can we solve it?

Today you will continue to develop ways to apply your problem solving techniques to solve wor problems as you examine a new type of problem: percent mixture problems.

12*45.   GET OUT THE VOTE

In an election for school President, 40% of 7th graders and 90% of 8th graders voted for John. If 1,000 students voted in the election, and if John ended up with 72% of the votes, how many students are in each grade at John's school? Assume that John's school only contains 7th and 8th grades. Explain how you found your answer.

12*46.   This year, the math club decided to make candy gifts for graduates. They will mix Choco-nuts, which cost $1 per ounce, with Munchies, which cost $2 per ounce. They would like their candy bags to weigh 4 ounces and cost $5.40. How much of each ty of candy should be used per bag?

12*47.   Antoine works in the paint department at his local hardware store. He is trying to cre a new color of paint using two different colors in stock: powder blue, which is made with 2% blue (the rest is white), and spring blue, which is 10% blue (the rest is white He wants to end up with one gallon of paint made with 4% blue. How much of each color should he use?

12*48.   As a Learning Reflection, describe what you know about solving percent mixture problems. Explain in your own words how to set up an equation or use Guess and Check to help solve this type of problem. Be sure to include an example. Title this entry "Percent Mixture Problems" and include today's date.

2*49.   How much coffee costing $6 a pound should be mixed with 3 pounds of coffee costing $4 per pound to create a mixture costing $4.75 per pound?

2*50.   If $g(x) = \sqrt{x - 3} + 1$, then find the values below. If there is no solution, **justify** your conclusion.

   a. $g(7)$ b. $g(4)$ c. $g(8)$ d. $g(2)$

2*51.   Graph the function $f(x) = |x - 3| - 1$ and label all its special points.

2*52.   Add, subtract, multiply, or divide the expressions below. Leave your answer as simplified as possible. Assume the denominators do not equal zero.

   a. $\dfrac{5}{x} - \dfrac{10}{x^2 + 2x}$

   b. $\dfrac{x^2 - 9}{x^2 + 6x + 9} \div \dfrac{x^2 - x - 6}{x^2 + 4}$

   c. $6 + \dfrac{3}{x+1}$

   d. $\dfrac{4x^2 - 13x + 3}{5x^2 + 23x - 10} \cdot \dfrac{5x - 2}{x^2 + 6x - 27} \cdot \dfrac{x^2 + 5x - 36}{4x - 1}$

2*53.   Find the point(s) of intersection of the line and parabola below. Be sure to check each point by substituting it back into both equations.

$$y = 3x^2 - 5x + 2$$
$$y = 4x + 2$$

2*54.   Solve the following quadratic equations by completing the square, if possible. Leave your answers in <u>exact</u> form. Check your solution(s).

   a. $x^2 - 14x = -24$

   b. $x^2 + 6x - 9 = 0$

   c. $x^2 - 198x + 9797 = 0$

   d. $x^2 - 9x = 15.75$

12.3.1 How can we derive it?

$$x = \frac{-b \pm \sqrt{b^2 - 4ac}}{2a}$$

In Chapter 9 you learned how to solve quadratic equations with the Quadratic Formula and the Zero Product Property. At the time, you had not yet learned how to complete the square of a quadratic equation and thus were not able to derive the Quadratic Formula by completing the square. You now have the tools to derive the Quadratic Formula by completing the square. To do this you will start with the equation $ax^2 + bx + c = 0$ and will solve for x to prove that:

$$x = \frac{-b \pm \sqrt{b^2 - 4ac}}{2a}$$

12*55.   DERIVATION OF THE QUADRATIC FORMULA

The steps below outline a proof that if $ax^2 + bx + c = 0$, then $x = \frac{-b \pm \sqrt{b^2 - 4ac}}{2a}$.

Fold a piece of lined paper in half vertically, make a crease, then unfold the paper. Copy the algebraic steps shown below onto the left-hand side of your paper. Write y‍ answer to each question to the right of the corresponding algebraic step.

We want to solve the equation $ax^2 + bx + c = 0$.

1. $ax^2 + bx = -c$ What did we do to get this?

2. $x^2 + \frac{b}{a}x = -\frac{c}{a}$ What did we do to get this?

Now we will complete the square.

3. $x^2 + \frac{b}{a}x + \frac{b^2}{4a^2} = \frac{b^2}{4a^2} - \frac{c}{a}$ Why did we choose $\frac{b^2}{4a^2}$?

4. $(x + \frac{b}{2a})^2 = \frac{b^2}{4a^2} - \frac{c}{a}$ What did we do to get this?

5. $(x + \frac{b}{2a})^2 = \frac{b^2 - 4ac}{4a^2}$ What did we do to get this?

We are very close! We now solve for x.

6. $x + \frac{b}{2a} = \pm \frac{\sqrt{b^2 - 4ac}}{2a}$ Why is there a "$\pm$" symbol?

7. $x = -\frac{b}{2a} \pm \frac{\sqrt{b^2 - 4ac}}{2a}$ What did we do to get this?

Finally, we get to the solution.

8. $x = \frac{-b \pm \sqrt{b^2 - 4ac}}{2a}$ What did we do to get this result?

512   Algebra Connections: Chapter

12*56.   Use the Quadratic Formula to solve the following quadratic equations. Be sure to check your solution(s), if possible.

a. $8x^2 + 14x - 15 = 0$

b. $5m + 0.5m^2 - 3 = 0$

c. $k^2 - 10k = -30$

d. $4x^2 - 25 = 0$

12*57.   Solve the quadratics below by first completing the square. Leave your solutions in exact form.

a. $x^2 - 10x + 22 = 0$

b. $x^2 + 2x = 18$

12*58.   Ms. Speedi's favorite recipe for fruit punch requires 12% apple juice. How much pure apple juice should she add to 2 gallons of punch that has 8% apple juice to meet her standards?

12*59.   Graph the function $g(x) = \sqrt{x - 3} + 1$. Describe its domain and range.

12*60.   Use the graph of $f(x)$ at right to find the following values.

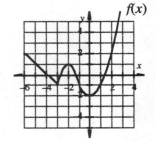

a. $f(1)$

b. $f(-6)$

c. $f(0)$

d. $f(-3)$

12*61.   Factor the quadratics below using any method.

a. $x^2 - 81$

b. $x^2 + 12x + 36$

c. $4x^2 - 4x - 3$

d. $16x^2 - 25$

12*62.   Where do the two parabolas below intersect?

$$y = x^2 + 4x - 2$$
$$y = x^2 - 3x + 5$$

12*63.   Rewrite each expression below.

a. $\sqrt{9} \cdot \sqrt{9}$

b. $\sqrt{2} \cdot \sqrt{2}$

c. $\sqrt{500} \cdot \sqrt{500}$

d. $\sqrt{x} \cdot \sqrt{x}$

12.4.1 How can we make a prediction?

Using Data and Trend Lines to Make Predictions

In today's lesson, you will use data to make a prediction. As you work, remember to find all the **connections** you can between different representations.

12*64.   THE BURNING CANDLE

Today is your friend's birthday. You want to surprise her by walking into the room carrying a piece of cake with a lit candle. However, you only have one candle and you are not sure it will stay lit long enough. Can you predict when the candle will burn out?

Your Task: Collect data for your burning candle that will help you predict when it will burn out. Collect data for at least two minutes. Then analyze the data and make a prediction. Your analysis must include:

- At least three representations of the data.

- An explanation of how you can use the equation to determine when the candle will burn out.

Discussion Points

What data should we collect as the candle burns?

Can we represent the candle data on a graph?

What information do we need to write an equation for the data?

How can we use our equation to determine when the candle will burn out?

Further Guidance

12*65.   Start by collecting data from the burning candle. Record its weight at various times after it has started to burn. (The candle's weight is easier and safer to measure than its height.) Make sure you let the candle burn for at least two minutes, and make sure you get at least five data points. When all the data is collected, blow the candle out.

12*66.   Let x represent the time (in seconds) since the candle started to burn, and let y represent the weight of the candle. Make an $x \to y$ table showing the data you collected for the burning candle.

12*67.   With your team, decide how the axes should be scaled for a graph of the candle data. Then graph the data you have collected. Agree with your teammates on a trend line that best fits the data, and add it to your graph.

12*68.   Now you will use your trend line to determine when the candle will burn out.

    a.   Write the equation for your trend line.

    b.   What do you know about the point on the graph at which the candle burns out? Do you know the value of either x or y at this point?

    c.   Use your equation and your answer to part (c) to solve for the time when the candle will burn out.

Review & Preview

12*69.   A line passes through the points (12.3, –3.4) and (34.2, 14.8).

    a.   Find the equation of the line.

    b.   Find the x-intercept of the line.

12*70.   Evaluate the expression below when $x = 27$ and $y = 16$.

$$6x^{2/3}y^{1/4} \cdot x^{-1}y^{1/2}$$

12*71.   Graph the function $h(x) = -\sqrt{3-x}$. Use inequalities to describe its domain and range.

12*72.   If $f(x) = \frac{-5}{x+2}$ and $g(x) = (x-2)^3$, find each output value below (if possible). If it is not possible, explain why not.

    a. $f(-2)$ b. $g(-1)$ c. $g(4)$ d. $f(-7) + g(1)$ e. $f(3) - g(2)$

12*73.   James used the Distributive Property and got $6m - 12$. Find an expression that he could have started with.

12*74.   Find all the points at which the parabolas below intersect. Write your solution(s) in (x, y) form.

$$y = x^2 - x + 12$$
$$y = 2x^2 + 3x + 7$$

12.4.2 What do we know about the pattern?

Remember tile patterns? When you first studied tile patterns, most of the patterns you studied grew in a linear fashion. Now you have the tools to analyze more complex patterns, applying what you know about non-linear equations. Today your team will use multiple representations to analyze and make predictions about a complex tile pattern.

12*75.   TEAM PATTERN CHALLENGE

Your teacher will assign your team a tile pattern to analyze today.

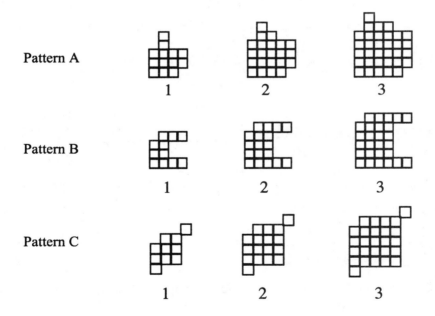

Your Task: With your team, analyze your pattern completely. Create a stand-alone poster showing the following.

Continued on next page →

12*75. *Continued from previous page*

Pattern Analysis:

- Figures 0 through 4.
- An $x \rightarrow y$ table.
- A sketch and description of the 100th figure.
- A rule for the xth figure.
- Connections between all of the representations of your pattern.

Using the Rule:

- How can you rewrite your rule? Use algebra to simplify your rule.

  Use your rule to make predictions about figures in your pattern that you cannot draw.

    o How many tiles are in figure 538?

    o <u>Pattern A</u>: Which figure will have 555,022 tiles?

    o <u>Pattern B</u>: Which figure will have 491,403 tiles?

    o <u>Pattern C</u>: Which figure will have 608,401 tiles?

12*76. If a tile pattern can be described by the equation $y = (x-1)(x+1) + x + 2$, where x represents the figure number and y represents the number of tiles, find each of the following.

a. The number of tiles in Figure 307.

b. The number of the figure that contains 169,333 tiles.

12*77. Solve the equations and inequalities below. Write your solutions in exact form.

a. $\frac{3}{4} - \frac{x}{3} = \frac{7-x}{4}$

b. $(b-4)^2 < 12$

c. $|3+x| - 9 \leq 21$

d. $5n^2 - 11n + 2 = 0$

12*78.   Graph the following quadratic by finding the roots and the vertex.

$$y = 3x^2 - 10x + 2$$

12*79.   For $f(x) = \frac{x^2}{x+5}$ and $g(x) = \sqrt{3x-2}$, find the following, if possible.

a. $f(6)$ b. $g(17)$ c. $f(-5)$ d. $g(-2)$

e. $g(-1) - f(2)$ f. $f(4) + g(2)$ g. $g(x+2)$ h. $f(x-1)$

12*80.   Add or subtract the following rational expressions. Then simplify your solutions, if possible. Assume the denominators do not equal zero.

a. $\frac{x-4}{2x^2+9x-5} + \frac{x+3}{x^2+5x}$ b. $\frac{4x^2-11x+6}{2x^2-x-6} - \frac{x+2}{2x+3}$

12*81.   If a tile pattern can be described by the equation $y = (x-1)(x+2) + x$, where x represents the figure number and y represents the number of tiles, find each of the following.

a.   The number of tiles in Figure 211.

b.   The number of the figure that contains 6,558 tiles.

12*82.   Erika can mow her family's lawn in 3 hours. Her little brother Mica can do it in 5 hours. How long will it take them to mow the lawn together?

12*83.   Graph the function $f(x) = \sqrt{|x-2|}$. Use inequalities to describe its domain and range.

12*84.   **Multiple Choice:** For which of the following equations or inequalities is $x = -1$ a solution?

a. $(x+3)^2 > 4$ b. $\frac{x+5}{2} = 2x^2$ c. $\sqrt{x+6} = 25$ d. $x^2 + 5x + 6 = 0$

12*85.   Find the equation of the line parallel to $3x + 2y = 10$ that goes through the point $(4, -7)$.

12.4.3 What do we know about the inequality?

Exploring an Inequality and its Corresponding Function

Over the course of this year, you have studied many different kinds of functions and inequalities—linear, quadratic, absolute values, square roots, and others. Today you will use the tools you have learned to analyze a new and interesting inequality.

12*86. The following inequality combines two functions you have studied to make a new kind of graph.

$$y > \left| 3 - 2x - x^2 \right| + 2$$

Your Task: With your team, create a **complete** description of the inequality.

Discussion Points

What does a complete description of an inequality include?

How can we graph the inequality?

How is this graph different from ones we have made before?

Does this graph have any special points?

Further Guidance

12*87. Start by graphing the function $f(x) = \left| 3 - 2x - x^2 \right| + 2$ on graph paper. Show all of your calculations. Decide if the curve should be solid or dashed.

12*88.   On your graph, shade the region containing the points that make the inequality $y > \left| 3 - 2x - x^2 \right| + 2$ true. Explain why you chose to shade the regions that you did.

12*89.   Describe this graph completely.

      a.   Does it have symmetry?

      b.   How could you describe its shape?

      c.   Does it have any special points? How many? Label these points on the graph with their coordinates.

12*90.   Imagine that you had to describe the graph of this inequality in words to someone who had never seen it. In full sentences, write exactly what you would tell them so that they could draw the same graph on their own graph paper.

Apply and Extend

12*91.   Does the point (–2, 4) make this inequality true? Explain how you know.

12*92.   For the function $f(x) = \left| 3 - 2x - x^2 \right| + 2$, find $f(4)$.

12*93.   Use your graph and rule to find every x-value for which $\left| 3 - 2x - x^2 \right| + 2 = 6$.

12*94. Is (−5, 7) a solution to $y < \sqrt{x^2 + 24}$?

12*95. The graphs of several relations are shown below. Decide if each is a function. If the relation is not a function, explain why not.

a.

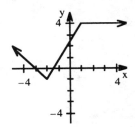

b.

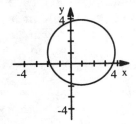

c.

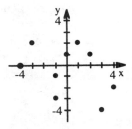

12*96. Solve the quadratics below by completing the square. Leave your solutions in exact form.

a. $x^2 - 6x - 12 = 0$

b. $x^2 - 3 = 4x$

12*97. Determine the number of solutions for each of the quadratics below. Note: You do not need to solve the quadratics.

a. $(x - 5)^2 = -6$

b. $312x^2 + 514x + 181 = 0$

c. $(x + 3)^2 - 10 = 0$

d. $4x^2 + 49 = 28x$

12*98. Jeremiah inherited his grandmother's very large coin collection. He has been giving away or selling the coins from the collection. The table at right shows the activity of his coin collection.

Year	# of Coins
2000	1617
2001	1552
2002	1498
2003	1453
2004	1401
2005	1344

a. Find the equation of a line that best fits Jeremiah's data.

b. At this rate, when should Jeremiah expect to be out of coins?

Algebraic Extensions

12.4.4 What is the largest area?

In this final lesson, you will **connect** and **apply** much of your knowledge from throughout the course to solve a challenging problem.

12*99.   FENCING LESSONS

Lucy wants to be a farmer, just like her dad. Her father says he will give her some cows to raise if she can build them a good pen. Lucy saves all her money and buys 30 meters of barbed wire. She will use it to build a rectangular pen against one wall of her family's barn, as shown in the picture at right.

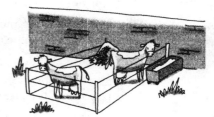

Lucy has come to you for help. She wants to build the best pen possible for her cows, giving them as much area as possible to roam. How long should each side of the fence be to give the cows as much roaming area as possible? How can you prove to Lucy that that pen is the largest?

Your Tasks:

- Create a poster showing all four representations of this situation.

- On your poster, include a drawing of the pen with the largest possible area. State its dimensions (width and height) and its area.

- Use multiple representations to **justify** your conclusion that this is the largest pen.

Discussion Points

What should x and y represent in this situation?

How can we collect and represent data about different-sized pens?

What kind of graph does this data make?

How does the best pen appear on the graph?

How can we represent the area in terms of x?

How can we use our equation to find the best possible fence dimensions?

12*100.   MAKING A TABLE

Start by trying out some different-sized pens, seeing which ones appear to give the largest area.

a.   Your teacher will show you how to use string to make examples of possible pens. Make one possible rectangular pen out of string and find the area it encloses.

b.   Start an $x \rightarrow y$ table for this situation. Let x be the length of the pen, and y be the enclosed area. Your first entry in the table should be the pen you just created.

c.   Use your string model to try out four other sets of pen dimensions. Calculate the area for each fence you try and enter your data into your table.

d.   Of all the pens you have tried so far, which dimensions have created the largest possible roaming area for the cows? Do you think this is the largest area possible? Why or why not?

12*101.   MAKING A GRAPH

Now you will graph the data you have collected and look for a trend.

a.   Draw and scale a set of axes for this situation. Be careful about how you scale your axes, so that all the possible pens will fit on your graph.

b.   Graph the data from your $x \rightarrow y$ table.

c.   Do you have a point on your graph where x is almost as big as it can possibly be? Do you have a point on your graph where x is almost as small as it can possibly be? If you are missing pens like these, build an example of each one using your string, enter the lengths and areas in your table, and plot the points on your graph.

d.   Make sure the x-intercepts are included on your graph. What do the roots of this graph represent?

12*102.   ANALYZING THE GRAPH

a.   Looking at the points you have plotted so far, can you see what the general shape of the graph will be? If so, sketch in what you think the whole graph should look like. If not, build some more pens with your string to fill in the sections of the graph where you do not have enough points. When you see the general shape of the graph, sketch it.

b.   Find the point on your graph representing the pen with the greatest area. What is the length of this pen?

c.   Use your graph to approximate the greatest possible enclosed area.

12*103.   WRITING AN EQUATION

a.   The length of Lucy's pen is x meters long, and she has only 30 meters of barbed wire. Use this information to write an expression for the width of the pen in terms of x.

b.   Now write an equation for y, the area of the space enclosed by the fence, in terms of x. Simplify your equation.

c.   What kind of graph should this equation have? Does it match your graph?

d.   Use your equation to find the roots of the graph. Do your results confirm the roots you found by looking at the graph?

e.   Use your equation to find the vertex of your graph. Does this point confirm the results you found by looking at the graph?

f.   Use your new results to find the largest possible roaming area Lucy can give her cows. What are the dimensions of this pen? Is this answer more precise than the one you got from your graph? How do you know?

12*104.   SHOWING YOUR WORK

Finally, put together a poster showing your work on this problem. Be sure to include all four representations of the situation. Use the equation and the graph to **justify** to Lucy which dimensions she should use.

12*105.   Find the minimum (the lowest point) of the function $f(x) = 3x^2 + 15x - 18$.

12*106.   Solve each equation.

a. $\sqrt{y^2 + 5} = y + 5$

b. $\frac{x^2 + x - 6}{x + 3} = \sqrt{8x - 7}$

12*107.   Find the equation of the line perpendicular to $3x - y = 4$ that goes through the point $(-12, 4)$.

12*108.   Graph the function $f(x) = \frac{5}{x-2}$. Use inequalities to describe its domain and range.

12*109.   How much candy costing $8 a pound should be mixed with 6 pounds of candy costing $10 a pound to create a mixture costing $8.50 a pound?

Glossary

absolute value   The absolute value of a number is the distance of the number from zero. Since the absolute value represents a distance, without regard to direction, it is always non-negative.

additive identity   The Additive Identity Property states that any term added to zero (0) remains unchanged; $a + 0 = a$. (p. 50)

additive inverse   The Additive Inverse Property states that when opposites are added, the result is always zero: $a + (-a) = 0$. (p. 66)

additive property of equality   The Additive Property of Equality states that equality is maintained if you add the same amount to both sides of an equation. If $a = b$, then $a + c = b + c$. (p. 240)

algebra tiles   The algebra tiles used in this course consist of large squares with dimensions x by x and y by y, rectangles with dimensions x by 1, and y by 1 and x by y and small squares with dimensions 1 by 1. The areas of these tiles are x^2, y^2, x, y, xy, and 1 respectively. We call the smallest squares unit squares. (p. 39)

area   For this course, area is the number of square units needed to fill up a region on a flat surface. The idea can be extended to cones, spheres, and more complex surfaces. (p. 9)

associative property   The Associative Property states that if a sum or product contains terms that are grouped, then the sum or product can be grouped differently with no effect on the result; $a + (b + c) = (a + b) + c$ and $a(bc) = (ab)c$. (p. 50)

average   See *mean*.

base   In the expression 2^5, 2 is called the base. Also, 5 is the exponent and 32 is the value. The term "base" may also refer to sides of a triangle, rectangle, parallelogram, trapezoid, prism, cylinder, pyramid, and cone.

binomial   The sum or difference of two monomials is called a binomial.

coefficient (numerical)   The numeral part of a term, such as 6 in $6x$. (p. 247)

common factor   Factors which are the same for two or more terms.

common term factoring   Factoring out a common (term) factor means identifying the common factor of the terms of a polynomial and then writing it outside the parentheses containing the sum of the factored terms. For example, $6x^2y - 9xy^2 = 3xy(2x - 3y)$. Factoring usually means using the Distributive Property: $ab + ac = a(b + c)$.

Commutative Property   The Commutative Property states that if two terms are added or multiplied, the order is reversible. $a + b = b + a$ and $ab = ba$. (p. 69)

complete graph   A complete graph has the following components: (1) the x-axis and y-axis labeled, clearly showing the scale. (2) Equation of the graph written near the line or curve. (3) Line or curve extended as far as possible on the graph. (4) x- and y- intercepts labeled. (5) Coordinates of points stated in (x, y) form. (p. 112)

completing the square   A method for solving quadratic equations or writing quadratic functions graphing form.

congruent   Two shapes (for example, triangles) are congruent if they have exactly the same size an shape.

conjecture   An educated guess, based on data, patterns, and relationships. Scientists use the term hypothesis.

constant   A symbol representing a value that does not change. For example, in the equation $y = 2x + 5$, "5" is referred to as the constant. (p. 247)

coordinate   The number paired with a point on the number line or an ordered pair (x, y) that corresponds to a point in an x, y -coordinate system. (p. 11)

coordinate system   A system of graphing ordered pairs of numbers in relation to axes (horizontal and vertical) that intersect at right angles at their zero points (origin). (p. 11)

corresponding parts   Points, edges (sides), or angles in congruent or similar figures that are arranged in similar ways. For instance if $\triangle ABC$ is similar to $\triangle XYZ$, side AB corresponds to (matches) the side XY.

degree (of a monomial or a polynomial)   (1) The degree of a monomial is the sum of the exponents of its variables, such as $3x^2y^5$ has degree 7;   (2) The degree of a polynomial is: (a) in on variable, the degree of the term with the highest exponent ($3x^5 - 4x^2 - x + 7$ has degree 5); (b) in more than one variable, the highest sum of the exponents among the terms, ($2x^5y^3 - 4x^2y^4z^3 - xy^5 + 3y^2z - 12$ has degree 9).

dependent variable   The output variable (y) of a relation or function is called the dependent variable because its values are determined by the value of x that is used in the relation or function.

diagram   A problem-solving technique based on drawing a picture or diagram representing the problem. Including all the known information on the diagram helps us to see what is important and necessary in solving the problem.

difference of squares   A special polynomial that can be factored as the product of the sum and difference of two terms. The general pattern is $x^2 - y^2 = (x + y)(x - y)$.

discriminant   For quadratic equations in standard form $ax^2 + bx + c = 0$, the discriminant is $b^2 -$

distributive property   For any numbers or expressions a, b, and c, $a(b + c) = ab + ac$. (p.188, 192)

dividing line (or boundary line)   A line on a two dimensional graph that divides the graph into two regions. We use a dividing line or boundary line when graphing linear inequalities such as $y > 3x - 1$.

dividing point   The endpoint of a segment on a number line where an inequality is true. For stric inequalities, that is, $<$ or $>$, the point is not part of the solution.

domain   The set of all input values for a relation or function. For variables, the set of numbers the variable may represent. For ordered pairs (x, y), all x-values.

elimination method (systems of equations)   A method for solving a system of equations by adding or subtracting the equations to eliminate one of the variables. (p. 241)

enlargement ratio   The ratio of similarity comparing a figure to a similar larger one is often called the enlargement ratio. This number tells you by what factor the first figure is enlarged by to get the second.

equal values method (systems of equations)   A method for solving a system of equations by setting two equivalent expressions (both equal to x or y) equal to each other and solving the resulting linear equation. (p. 166, 202)

equation   A mathematical sentence with an equal sign (=).

equation mat   An organizing tool to represent expressions that are equal. It is used to solve equations with algebra tiles. (p. 62, 63)

evaluate   To evaluate an expression, substitute the value(s) given for the variable(s) and perform the operations according to the order of operations. (p. 46)

exponent   In the expression 2^5, 5 is called the exponent. Also, 2 is the base and 32 is the value. The exponent indicates how many times to use the number 2 as a multiplier, in this case, times, $2 \cdot 2 \cdot 2 \cdot 2 \cdot 2 = 32$.

exponents (laws of)   There are several basic laws of exponents: (1) $x^a \bullet x^b = x^{a+b}$;

(2) $\dfrac{x^a}{x^b} = x^{a-b}$; (3) $(x^a)^b = x^{ab}$.

exponents (negative)   For any number $x \neq 0$, $x^{-n} = \dfrac{1}{x^n}$ and $\dfrac{1}{x^{-n}} = x^n$.

exponents (zero)   For any number $x \neq 0$, $x^0 = 1$.

expression   An algebraic expression consists of one or more variables. It may also contain some constants. Each part of the expression separated by addition or subtraction signs is called a term. (p.54)

factor   (1) In arithmetic: when two or more numbers are multiplied, each of the numbers is a factor of the product. (2) In algebra: where two or more algebraic expressions are multiplied together, each of the expressions is a factor of the product.

factored completely   A polynomial is factored completely if none of the resulting factors can be factored further.

Fibonacci Numbers   The numbers in the sequence 1, 1, 2, 3, 5, 8, 13, ... are called the Fibonacci Numbers. (p. 89)

F.O.I.L.   An approach for multiplying two binomials is to use the mnemonic "F.O.I.L." which stands for "First, Outer, Inner, Last." It describes the order in which to multiply the terms of two binomials to be sure to get all the products.

fraction busters   A method of simplifying equations involving fractions that uses the Multiplication Property of Equality to rearrange the equation so that no fractions remain.

function   A function is a relation in which for each input value there is one and only one output value. In terms of ordered pairs (x, y), no two ordered pairs have the same first member (x).

function notation   Functions are given names, most commonly "f", "g" or "h." The notation $f(x$ represents the output of a function, named f, when x is the input. It is pronounced "f of x". The notation $g(2)$ is pronounced "g of 2" and represents the output of the function g when $x = 2$.

generic rectangle   In this course, used as an organizational device for multiplying polynomials. example, the figure below shows how to use generic rectangles to multiply binomials. (p. 192, 213

$$(2x + 1)(x + 6) = 2x^2 + x + 12x + 6 = 2x^2 + 13x + 6$$

greatest common factor   (1) For integers, the greatest positive integer that is a common factor of two or more integers. (2) For two or more algebraic monomials, the product of the greatest commo integer factor of the coefficients of the monomials and the variable(s) in each algebraic term with th greatest degree of that variable in every term. For example, the greatest common factor of $12x^3y^2$ a $8xy^4$ is $4xy^2$. (3) For a polynomial, the greatest common monomial factor of its terms. For exampl the greatest common factor of $16x^4 + 8x^3 + 12x$ is $4x$.

growth factor   For a linear relationship, the amount the y- value changes, when the x- value increases by one. (p. 199)

growth number   See *growth factor*.

guess and check   Guess and check is a problem solving strategy in which you begin by making a guess and then check whether or not your guess is correct. In the process of checking, you gain information about how close your guess might be and make adjustments to your guess. The second guess is then tested. This continues until the correct answer is discovered. Being organized is crucial to the success of this method, as well as writing a usable table. Guess and check also leads us to writing equations to represent word problems. (p. 22-23, 97)

horizontal lines   Horizontal lines are "flat" and run left to right in the same direction as the x-axi All horizontal lines have equations of the form $y = b$, where b can be any number. Their slope is 0. The x-axis has the equation $y = 0$ because $y = 0$ everywhere on the x-axis.

hypothesis   A conjecture is what mathematicians call an educated guess, based on data, patterns, a relationships. Scientists use the term hypothesis.

identity element   The identity element for addition is 0 because adding 0 leaves the number unchanged: $a + 0 = 0$. The identity element for multiplication is 1, because multiplying by 1 leaves number unchanged: $a(1) = a$. (p. 50)

independent variable   The input variable (x), of a relation or function is called the independent variable.

inequality symbols   The symbol "$\leq$" read from left to right means "less than or equal to." The symbol "$\geq$" read from left to right means "greater than or equal to." The symbols $<$ and $>$ mean "less than" and "greater than" respectively.

input value In a relation or function where $y = f(x)$, the values used for x (the domain) and substituted into the relationship are the input values. The input values are the numbers represented by the independent variables, the first numbers in ordered pairs (x, y).

integers The set of numbers $\{ \ldots -3, -2, -1, 0, 1, 2, 3, \ldots \}$.

inverse operations Addition and subtraction are inverse operations, as are multiplication and division.

irrational numbers The set of numbers that cannot be expressed in the form $\frac{a}{b}$ where a and b are integers and $b \neq 0$. For example, π and $\sqrt{2}$ are irrational numbers.

justify To use facts, definitions, rules, and/or previously proven statements in an organized way to convince your audience that what you claim (or your answer) is valid (true).

like terms Two or more terms that contain the same variable(s), with corresponding variables raised to the same power are called like terms. For example, $5x$ and $2x$ are like terms. Combine like terms by adding them: $5x + 2x = (5 + 2)x = 7x$. (p. 54)

linear equation Any equation equivalent to $ax + by = c$ (standard form), where a, b, and c are real numbers and a and b are not both zero. Slope-intercept form, $y = mx + b$, is one equivalent form. (p. 199)

linear graphs Graphs that are straight lines are called linear graphs.

mean The mean (average) of several numbers (or data points) is a statistical measurement that describes one way of defining the middle of the numbers. It is found by adding the numbers together and dividing by the number of data points in the set. (p. 64)

monomial An expression with only one term. It can be a numeral, a variable, or the product of a number and one or more variables. For example, 7, $3x$, $-4ab$, or $3x^2y$ are each monomials.

multiplicative identity The Multiplicative Identity Property states that any term multiplied by one (1) remains unchanged; $a(1) = a$. (p. 50)

multiplicative inverse The Multiplicative Inverse Property states that when multiplying a term by its reciprocal, the result is always one: $a \cdot \frac{1}{a} = 1$ and $\frac{a}{b} \cdot \frac{b}{a} = 1$ (for a not equal to 0). (p. 50)

multiplying binomials See *generic rectangle*. (p. 213)

neutral field The number 0 can be represented by the same number of positive and negative tiles, known as a neutral field. (p. 5)

numeral A symbol that names a number.

numerical coefficient See *coefficient*.

opposite The opposite of a number is its additive inverse. For example, -5 is the opposite of 5. (p. 66)

ordered pairs Points on the x,y coordinate grid written as (x, y). The first coordinate (x) represents the horizontal distance and direction from the origin; the second coordinate (y) represents the vertical distance and direction from the origin. (p. 11)

order of operations   We use the order of operations to simplify complex arithmetic and algebraic expressions, by performing certain operations in a specific order. The order is: parentheses (or other grouping symbols), exponents (powers or roots), multiplication and division (left to right), and addition and subtraction (left to right). (p. 58)

origin   The point assigned to zero on the number line or the point where the x- and y-axes intersect in a coordinate system, denoted by the coordinates $(0, 0)$. (p. 208)

output values   In a relation or function where $y = f(x)$, the y-values (range) are the output values.

parabola (equation from its x-intercepts)   A parabola with x-intercepts $(b, 0)$ and $(c, 0)$ can be written in the form: $y = a(x - b)(x - c)$. The coefficient (a) determines the shape (wide or narrow) and the direction (open upward or downward) of the parabola.

parabolic graphs   Graphs of quadratic equations are parabolas and are called parabolic. (p. 101)

percent   A notation for a ratio with the denominator 100.

perfect square trinomials   Trinomials of the form $x^2 + 2ax + a^2$ are known as perfect square trinomials and factor as $(x + a)^2$.

perimeter   Perimeter is the distance around a figure on a flat surface. (p. 5)

perpendicular   Two lines or segments on a flat surface meet (intersect) to form a 90° angle.

polynomial   The sum or difference of two or more monomials.

power   A number or variable raised to an exponent in the form x^n. See *exponent*.

probability   Probability is a mathematical way to predict how likely it is that an event will occur. all the outcomes of an event are equally likely to occur, then the probability (or likelihood) that a specified result occurs is expressed by the fraction:

$$P(\text{event}) = \frac{number\ of\ outcomes\ in\ the\ specified\ event}{total\ number\ of\ possible\ outcomes}$$

problem solving strategies   This course deals with numerous problem solving strategies, specifically, making a guess and checking it, using manipulatives (such as algebra tiles), making systematic lists, collecting data, graphing, drawing a diagram, breaking a large problem into smaller subproblems, working backward, and writing and solving equations.

proportion   An equation stating that two fractions (or ratios) are equal. (p. 206-208)

quadratic   A polynomial is quadratic if the largest exponent in the polynomial is two (that is, the polynomial has degree 2).

quadratic equation (standard form)   A quadratic equation is in standard form if it is written as $ax^2 + bx + c = 0$.

quadratic formula   If $ax^2 + bx + c = 0$ and $a \neq 0$, then $x = \dfrac{-b \pm \sqrt{b^2 - 4ac}}{2a}$.

radical   An expression in the form $\sqrt{a}$ (square root). Other roots, such as cube root, will be studied in other courses.

radical (simplified form) A number $r\sqrt{s}$ is in simple radical form if no square of an integer divides s and s is not a fraction; that is, there are no more perfect square factors (square numbers such as 4, 9, 16, etc.) under the radical sign and no radicals in the denominator. For example, $5\sqrt{12}$ is not a simple radical form since 4 (the square of 2) divides 12. But $5\sqrt{12} = 10\sqrt{3}$ is in simple radical form.

radicand The expression under the radical sign.

range The set of all second members of a function or relation, that is, all possible output values for a relation or function. For ordered pairs (x, y), all output (y) values.

ratio A ratio is a comparison of two quantities by division. (p. 206)

ratio of similarity The ratio of similarity between any two similar figures is the ratio of any pair of corresponding sides. In this course ratios will always be listed in the order that compares the "new" to the "original" figure.

rational expression An expression in the form of a fraction in which the numerator and/or denominator contain polynomials.

rational numbers Numbers that can be expressed in the form $\frac{a}{b}$ where a and b are integers, $\neq 0$.

ratio of similar figures The ratio of similarity between any two similar figures is the ratio of any pair of corresponding sides. This means that once it is determined that two figures are similar, all of their pairs of corresponding sides have the same ratio.

real numbers Irrational numbers together with rational numbers form the set of the real numbers. All real numbers are represented on the number line.

reciprocal The reciprocal of a non-zero number is its multiplicative inverse. For x, the reciprocal is $\frac{1}{x}$; for $\frac{a}{b}$, the reciprocal is $\frac{b}{a}$. (p. 66)

rectangular numbers The numbers in the pattern 2, 6, 12, 20, ... are known as the rectangular numbers.

reduction ratio The ratio of similarity comparing a figure to a similar smaller one is often called the reduction ratio. This number tells you by what factor the first figure is reduced to get the second.

reference point When solving equations involving absolute values, it is sometimes useful to start with a reference point. For an equation such as $|x - a| = b$, a is the reference point. After locating the point a on a number line, we find the numbers which are a distance of b from a. This usually gives us the two solutions to the equation.

reflexive property The Reflexive Property states that a term is always equal to itself: $a = a$.

relation An equation which relates inputs to outputs is called a relation. As such, a relation is a set of ordered pairs. The set of first values is the domain, the set of second values is the range.

roots of an equation A solution of the equation. The x-intercepts of a parabola are also referred to as the roots of the quadratic equation.

scientific notation   A number is expressed in scientific notation when it is in the form $a \cdot 10^n$, where $1 \le a < 10$ and n is an integer.

similar figures   Similar geometric figures are figures that have the same shape but are not necessarily the same size. In similar figures, the measures of corresponding angles are equal and t lengths of corresponding sides have the same ratio. (p. 72)

simplest form (of a numerical expression)   The simplest way to express a value equivalent to a numerical expression.

simplest form (of a variable expression)   An expression equivalent to an original expression, l expressed in simplest form. A variable expression in simplest form has no like terms and no parentheses.

slope   The slope of a line is a ratio that describes how steep (or flat) the line is. Slope can be positive, negative, or even zero, but a straight line has only one slope. Slope is the ratio $\frac{\text{change in y value}}{\text{change in x value}}$ or $\frac{\text{vertical change}}{\text{horizontal change}}$. The symbol used to represent slope is the letter "m." Som texts refer to slope as the ratio of the "rise over the run." A line has positive slope if it slopes upwa from left to right on a graph; negative slope if it slopes downward from left to right. A vertical line has undefined or no slope.

slope-intercept form   Any non-vertical line can be described by an equation written in the form $y = mx + b$. The "m" represents the slope of the line (it is the coefficient of x). The "b" represents y-value of the y-intercept (where $x = 0$). Ordered pairs (x, y) that make the equation true are coordinates of points on that line. (p. 142, 199)

slope triangle   A slope triangle is a right triangle drawn on a graph of a line so that the hypotenuse of the triangle is part of the line. The vertical leg length is the change in the y-value; the horizontal leg length is the change in the x-value. The length of the legs of the triangle are the value used in the slope ratio (change in y : change in x).

solution   A replacement for the variable that makes an open sentence (equation) true.

solve   Find the solution(s) of equations or inequalities. (p. 61-62, 165, 233, 241)

square numbers   The numbers in the pattern 1, 4, 9, 16, 25, ..., that is, the squares of the countin numbers 1, 2, 3, 4, 5, ..., are known as square numbers.

standard form (of a linear equation)   See *linear equation*.

standard notation   A number written out completely, showing all digits and without use of exponents is written in standard notation.

subproblem   Breaking down problems into smaller, simpler parts is a technique for solving problems. The smaller, simpler problems are called subproblems. Solving the simpler, smaller problems first allows us to then put the results together to complete a larger problem.

substitution   Replacing one symbol by another (a number, a variable, or other algebraic expressi without changing the value of the expression.

ubstitution method (systems of equations) A method of solving a system of equations by ‑placing one variable with an expression involving the remaining variable(s). One variable is ⟨pressed in terms of the other variable, such as y-form, that is, $y = mx + b$, then the expression $x + b$ replaces that variable (y) in a second equation involving x and y. (p. 233)

ubstitution property If $a = b$, then either a or b can be replaced by the other.

ymmetric property The Symmetric Property states that if two terms are equal it does not ‑atter which is stated first. If $a = b$ then $b = a$.

ystems of linear equations For this course, two equations in two variables that describe ‑nes that may or may not intersect. The equations together are called a system of equations and ⟨e process of finding where, if at all, the lines intersect is called solving the system. (p. 244)

‑rm Each part of the expression separated by addition or subtraction signs is called a term. (p. 54)

‑iangular numbers The numbers in the pattern 1, 3, 6, 10, 15, ... are known as triangular ‑umbers.

‑ansitive property of equality The Transitive Property of Equality states that if $a = b$ and $b = c$, ‑en $a = c$.

‑inomial A polynomial of three terms.

wo-point graphing method Using only two points to graph a linear equation. Often one of the ‑oints is the y-intercept, but it does not need to be.

alue In the expression 2^5, 32 is the value. Also, 5 is the exponent and 2 is the base.

ariable For this course a variable is a symbol used in a mathematical sentence to represent a ‑umber.
⟩. 39)

ertex (of a parabola) The highest point or lowest point on a parabola (depending on its ‑rientation) is called the vertex. (p. 101)

ertical lines Vertical lines run up and down in the same direction as the y-axis and parallel to it. ‑ll vertical lines have equations of the form $x = a$, where a can be any number. The y-axis has the ‑quation $x = 0$ because $x = 0$ everywhere on the y-axis. Vertical lines have undefined slope.

vorking backward In many cases, to solve a problem we must "undo" something that has been ‑done." This is true when we solve equations. The notion of being able to "undo" something is part ⟨f the problem solving strategy of working backward and the mathematical operation is called an ‑verse operation. Working backwards uses inverse operations to find the original form of an ⟨xpression or value(s) of a variable. Solving an equation is an example of this process.

‑axis The horizontal axis on a coordinate plane (graph) is called the x-axis. (p. 11)
‑coordinate The first component (coordinate) in an ordered pair.

‑intercepts The point(s) where a graph crosses the x-axis is (are) called the x-intercepts. The x‑ntercept always has coordinates $(x, 0)$. (p. 112)

‑axis The vertical axis on a coordinate plane (graph) is called the y-axis. (p. 11)

‑coordinate The second component (coordinate) in an ordered pair.

y-form   An equation is written in *y*-form if the equation is solved for *y*, and so is written as "*y* = _____". The *y*-form of a linear equation is $y = mx + b$. (p. 142, 199)

y-intercepts   The point(s) where the graph crosses the *y*-axis is (are) called the *y*-intercepts. The *y*-intercept always has a coordinate $(0, y)$. (p. 112)

zero product property   The Zero Product Property states that when the product of two or more factors is zero, one of these factors must equal zero; that is, if $a \bullet b = 0$ then either $a = 0$ or $b = 0$. Note that we can use the Zero Product Property to solve quadratic equations that are factorable.

List of Symbols

+	plus (addition)		$\sqrt{}$	square root
-	minus (subtraction)		1:5	1 to 5 ratio
$\bullet$	times (multiplication)		$\pm$	plus or minus
$\div$	divide by (division)		>	greater than
-1	negative one (negative integer)		<	less than
=	equals		$\geq$	greater than or equal to
(x, y)	the point x-y, coordinates of a point		$\leq$	less than or equal to
$y = mx + b$	slope-intercept form of a linear equation		x^2	x squared

◪   represents 1

☐   represents -1

▭ *x*   represents *x*

▢ x^2 represents x^2

▭ *y*   represents *y*

▢ y^2 represents y^2

▭ *xy*   represents *xy*

Index

Many of the pages referenced here contain a definition or example of the topic listed, often within the body of a Math Notes box. The page numbers in bold represent where the topic is explicitly defined. Other referenced pages contain problems that develop or demonstrate the topic. It may be necessary to read the text preceding or following a problem, or additional problems to understand the topic fully. Also, some problems listed here are good examples of the topic and do not offer any direct explanation.